'I'm not interested declared firmly. 'I' night stands even in a one-horse town like this.'

He got angry then. Tamara wouldn't have thought it was possible for this large, oafish male to suddenly appear dangerous, but she hadn't noticed quite how broad his shoulders were in their covering of brown suede until they were being hunched so formidably over her.

Tamara shifted uncomfortably. 'Sorry, I didn't mean to insult your city.'

'What about insulting me?'

Why did men take things so personally?

'What makes you think,' he said, 'that I would want to go to bed with a scrawny woman who wears ridiculous clothes, has hair the colour of grated carrots and a personality that would make a lemon pucker?'

It took a lot to render Tamara speechless, but now it was her turn to gape.

'You're not my type, Tamara Clark. You're not my type at all!'

Claire Harrison was born in Brooklyn, New York and spent her first nineteen years in a small town which had once been a whaling village on the north shore of Long Island. She is happily married to a tall, dark and handsome man she met while at university in Binghamton and they have two daughters. Always a compulsive 'scribbler of short stories and poems', her first romance novel appeared in 1979. Six years and seventeen romance publications later sees Claire Harrison and her family living in Ottawa where, along with her novel writing, she prepares book reviews and articles for *The Washington Post*. Her documentary on 'The Romantic Fantasy' won her a Best Radio Program award. WILD FLOWER is Claire Harrison's second novel for Worldwide and is a sequel to ARCTIC ROSE.

WILD FLOWER

BY

CLAIRE HARRISON

WORLDWIDE ROMANCE

London ● Sydney ● Toronto

First published in Hardback in 1986
by Worldwide Romance,
15–16 Brook's Mews, London W1A 1DR

This Paperback edition published in 1986
by Worldwide Romance

Extract from *Medea* by Euripides in a translation by Philip Vellacott on pages 276 and 277 by kind permission of Penguin Books Limited.

Australian copyright 1986
Philippine copyright 1986

© Claire Harrison 1986

ISBN 0 373 50299 0

09/0586–74,200

Set in 11 on 12 pt Linotron Palatino

Photoset by Rowland Phototypesetting Limited
Bury St Edmunds, Suffolk
Printed and bound in Great Britain by
Cox & Wyman Ltd, Reading

PROLOGUE

A MAN lay naked on the four-poster bed, his silvery-blond head against the delicate white eyelet pillow sham, the lower half of his body covered by a sheet. He was a big man with heavy broad shoulders, bulging muscles in his arms and large, square hands. The colour of his moustache was a reddish-brown while the hair on his chest, thick and curly, was a deep gold. He had dark-brown eyes, a nose that had been the brunt of one too many adolescent fist fights and a blunt chin. He was not, by most standards, considered handsome. His appeal for the opposite sex lay in a lazy smile and a genuine and amiable appreciation of women.

Even now, when he was aroused and waiting for the woman who was brushing out her hair at the mirror on the other side of the room, Jake DeBlais was relaxed. His arms were folded behind his head, his legs were crossed at the ankles. He was humming to himself, staring up at the canopy of white eyelet over his head and thinking what a useless thing it was. What would they have called it in the old days? A frippery—that's what it was—a feminine indulgence for the non-essential. A stretch of fabric that collected dust and obstructed his view of the ceiling. A small smile curved under Jake's moustache as he contemplated the nature of women. He hadn't met one yet that didn't like pretty, useless things like bracelets and necklaces, scarves and flowers, ruffles and pleats.

Women were as predictable as the sunrise, Jake thought, and wondered why so many men found them mysterious. He had always understood them; maybe it came of having known so many. He knew what pleased a woman, he knew how to say the flowery things that made her eyes go soft and when to touch her hand at dinner to inspire that feeling of intimacy. He knew how to talk to a woman and to communicate to her his respect, his interest and the fact that he found her adorable and sexy and desirable. And he loved that moment when the sensual connection was made and the knowledge of the love-making to come would hover over the evening like a warm, golden glow.

Take the woman who was standing before the mirror, and Jake's eyes turned towards her as she unbuttoned her blouse, her long dark hair falling down her back like a gleaming curtain. He had met her two weeks ago at a party, one of those crowded, Calgary cocktail gatherings of oil and gas people where the conversation was superficial and the food left him hungry. He had caught sight of her in a group of people, a tall woman with a slender nose and slanting green eyes. He had walked over and introduced himself. Within minutes, they had sized one another up. He was unmarried, footloose and fancy-free; she was divorced and had one small child who was staying with her ex-husband for the weekend. Two hours later they had been in bed together, hers, and the pattern had been established. Despite the fact that Jake felt slightly uncomfortable surrounded by eyelet and lace, he had accepted the situation. Women's bedrooms were all alike anyway; floral and feminine, letting a man know that he was there by invitation only.

'My son's coming home tomorrow morning,' the woman said as she pulled off her blouse.

'I'll leave early,' Jake replied. 'I have to be at work at the crack of dawn anyway.'

Her voice was hesitant, questioning. 'You don't want to meet him?'

Jake met her glance in the mirror. 'I don't think it's a good idea, do you?'

Her eyes dropped as she fumbled with the catch of her skirt. 'I suppose it isn't.'

He leaned up on his elbow. 'Need some help with that?' he asked, hoping to ease the hurt of his rebuff. He knew what had been in her mind when she had asked him if he would like to meet her son. She had wanted to expand their relationship from the sexual to the familial; she had wanted to include Jake in the daily routine of her life. It was a gesture he had known would come from her eventually; she wasn't any different from the others in that respect.

They all wanted the same thing in the end; they all thought that Jake was suffering from a bachelor malaise and that he would want to meet their children, their mothers, their friends. He had learned, long ago, to nip that nurturing

instinct in the bud so that it wouldn't blossom
into an emotion more dangerous or insistent.
Jake wasn't in the market for a long-term relationship or a wife. He shied away from anything that
smacked of commitment or responsibility where
a woman was concerned. Life was easier that
way, he thought, and far more pleasant.

Most of the women he slept with caught on to
the rules of his game quickly enough and, fortunately, this one was no different. She was sensitive enough to gauge the lie of the land and now
deliberately lightened the atmosphere with a
flirtatious glance. 'Skilful at zippers, are you?'

'I've had a bit of practice,' he said.

She walked towards him, her breasts full and
bound in the wisps of lace, the rub of her stock-
inged legs making a soft, silken sound. The lamp
light was golden and put reddish gleams in her
dark hair. Jake felt the heat rise within him, focus
on his groin and swell his flesh.

She smiled down at him, seductive and enticing, her perfume delicately scenting the air.
'Want to practise on me?' she asked softly.

He grinned at her then and reached up to pull
her down on the bed beside him. The sheet
slipped off, revealing all of him; the muscularity
of his legs, the flat abdomen and the dark-gold
filaments of pubic hair gleaming around the
thick sword of flesh. 'I was wondering,' he
drawled, 'if you'd ever ask.'

CHAPTER ONE

In the end, it wasn't the many letters that she had received from Rebecca or the invitations or even the offers of money to pay her plane fare that persuaded Tamara to fly to Calgary to visit her sister. It was the exhaustion, the bone-deep and unending fatigue that made her legs tremble as if they couldn't hold her up any more and caused her powers of concentration to flag so that she forgot her lines and stumbled over names and couldn't remember where she had put anything. It was a feeling that Tamara had never had before. She was a high-energy person and accustomed to a hectic and gruelling routine; she was used to running from morning to night, to ignoring her body and expecting it to function perfectly. She had never anticipated that a time would come when her strength would suddenly collapse as if the burden of so much overwork and so little sleep had overwhelmed it.

At least, that's what Tamara attributed the bouts of weariness to and the now more than occasional dizzy spell. She had worn herself down, racing from dancing class to singing lesson to that new course in acting. She had sacrificed her rest so that she could have time to go to auditions, working late hours as a waitress and spending whatever free time she had shopping for bargains. When you lived so close to the poverty line, survival was a matter of time. She had stood for hours on lines to get discounted tickets to Broadway shows; she would go blocks uptown to cash in a food coupon; she haunted every second-hand clothes store in New York to find what she wanted. Although Tamara didn't qualify as a successful actress, she knew how to dress for the part, and maintaining the façade took vast quantities of energy.

For the past month, however, she had realised that her body was rebelling. It was true she had taken on an extra jazz class and, in order to pay for it, she had started to work in a Jewish deli during the lunch-hour as a fast order cook and counter waitress. She had rationalised this second job as, not only a means to extra money, but also as a way to get a free meal. Tamara tended to exist on infusions of coffee and the occasional peanut butter and jelly sandwich. The only time this pattern changed was when she was in the midst of an affair. If her lover had money, it meant luxurious dinners out and elegant breakfasts tête-à-tête. The trouble was that the pickings had recently been slim, and Tamara's latest men had been as down-at-heel as she was.

The deli job had, therefore, seemed like the ideal solution. She hadn't eaten so well in a long time, gorging on bagels and cream cheese, thick sandwiches of corned beef on rye, hot bowls of matzoh ball soup, fragrant and steamy. But even the food, healthy and nutritious, was unable to provide her with enough sustenance for her physical needs. Tamara's body went right on failing her when she needed its co-operation the most. She missed classes because she would fall asleep on a bus; she arrived late at appointments because she was unable to keep track of the time; and, as a last straw, she had arrived at an important audition, thinking that she had her speech memorised and well-rehearsed, only to discover that it had flown out of her mind and disappeared into the thin air like a bird newly escaped from its cage.

She dragged herself out of bed in the mornings and had circles under her eyes so deep and pervasive that her boss, Mr Freiberg, took one look at her and sat her down on a stool in his office in the back of the deli. It had a floor strewn with sawdust, an old wooden desk and two hard-backed chairs. He sat Tamara down on one of them and himself on the other so that their knees almost touched. Then he took off his spectacles, wiped them on his apron and sighed. 'Are you getting enough sleep?' he asked. He was a man in his fifties with kind, brown eyes and a fringe of white hair.

Tamara was a consummate New Yorker; she was used to bluffing her way out of awkward situations even if it meant lying through her teeth. She gave Mr Freiberg her most charming smile. 'Last night,' she said, 'I got home and found that I didn't have my key. The super was out shopping so I couldn't get into my apartment until after midnight and . . .'

Mr Freiberg shook his head in disbelief. 'You don't look well.'

Tamara touched her cheeks where the blush from her make-up ran like a red streak across the pale skin over her cheekbones. 'It's the make-up; maybe it makes me look ghoulish.'

'And you're making mistakes,' he went on. 'The last customer you had got pastrami instead of corned beef, and Mrs Melkowitz, whom you have waited on a dozen times, does not take marmalade with her *latkes*. No one, Tamara, takes marmalade with *latkes*.'

'God, I'm sorry,' she apologised. 'I was thinking about my lines for that audition I have tomorrow, but that will be over soon and I can . . .'

'Look,' Mr Freiberg continued, leaning forward and patting one of her hands, 'I want you to go home, have a nice rest and come back in a week. I'm not firing you. You're a nice girl, the customers like you.'

'It's the audition. Really, it is. Once that's over I'll be home free.'

Mr Freiberg gave her a shrewd glance over the edge of his spectacles. 'You girls who want to make it on Broadway, you're all the same, you know. Burning the candle at both ends, not getting enough sleep, moonlighting. I've seen it all.'

'But . . .'

'You're not good for business; you look like death warmed up. Sweetheart, I want my waitresses to look *appetising* so the customers stay hungry.'

'But . . .'

'No buts,' he had said, his eyes still kind but firm. 'If it's money, I'll make you a loan. I'll advance you the wages for the week you come back. Now, off with that apron and get some sleep.'

No more free meals and Mr Freiberg's generous loan only meant that she would work the following week for nothing. After he had gone, Tamara slipped off her white apron with resignation and slowly loosened her hair from its enclosure of mesh. That meant that she would have to rely on tips from customers, not the most reliable or stable source of income. The jazz teacher had to be paid every week, and she had seen an old Persian lamb coat in the Next-to-New Shop on 23rd and Lexington that would make a fantastic dress coat. Most people thought that Persian lamb had been out of style since the Second World War, but Tamara had a way of wearing clothes that made the eye of the beholder blink with surprise. If she took Mr Freiberg's loan, she thought tiredly as she pulled on a skirt and blouse, and put a deposit on the coat, she could touch her friend Sheila for a few bucks to pay the jazz teacher. And, by the time Sheila wanted her money back, the jazz class would be over and she would have enough income from the deli job so that . . .

Tamara's head ached and buzzed when she reached her apartment, and she was almost too tired to open the letter that had arrived from her sister that morning. Rebecca was two years older

than she was, happily married and living in
Calgary. She had two children; a boy of five,
Kevin, and a new baby, Jennifer. She wrote
about walking the floor at night with Jennifer
who had colic, about baby rash and mountains
of Pampers. She wrote about Kevin's latest esca-
pades with his tricycle and her husband, Guy's,
newest business venture, the acquisition of an oil
exploration company.

Rebecca had ended the letter with her usual
request, asking Tamara to visit, offering to pay
her way and describing the guest-room that she
had waiting and available for Tamara's arrival in
poetic terms, a 'room decorated in cool and soothing blues with the sun shining through a window
that overlooks the sweeping grasses of the
prairie. It's not too close to Jennifer's room so you
wouldn't hear the baby crying and you'll have
your own private bathroom. All you have to do,
Tam, is sleep, eat and listen to me talk about the
children. I know it isn't as exciting as New York,
but it would be a change of pace and I'd love to
see you. Love, Becks. PS. And remember Guy's
partner, Jake? He's still unmarried and we could
set you up for some dates. I know you hate
matchmaking, but I wouldn't want you to think
that Calgary was the end of the world either.'

Tamara usually shoved Rebecca's letters into
her desk drawer and ignored them until a guilty
conscience prompted her to answer. It wasn't
that she didn't care about Rebecca or want to hear
from her. It was simply that Rebecca's life of
domestic happiness was so distant from hers that

Tamara felt as if they lived in totally different worlds. Rebecca had wanted a husband and children; Tamara wanted a career. Rebecca was retiring, peaceful and tactful; Tamara was intense, driven and outspoken. They had always got along as sisters but their relationship had been one of respectful opposites rather than close friends.

Yet she had always had the feeling that Rebecca would be only too happy if she could make Tamara over into her own mould. Happily married women were often like that, Tamara had noticed; they couldn't understand why the rest of the world didn't have a driving force to duplicate their own state of bliss. And, of course, she remembered Jake. In fact, Tamara had had Jake, metaphorically speaking, handed to her on a silver platter in numerous letters. She knew more about him, in some ways, than she knew about her friends. Rebecca had regaled her with stories of Jake's business acumen, nice personality, attractive looks and single state. Tamara had never laid eyes on the man, but it was clear that Rebecca thought that her sister and Guy's partner would be an ideal couple. Ignoring all disclaimers to the contrary, Rebecca was clearly set on a course of matchmaking. It amused Tamara and irritated her. She could just imagine what Rebecca conceived of as good husband material. A dull man, solid and respectable, with a steady job and a dream of a house and children and a dutiful little wife waiting gratefully by the sink for him to bring home the bacon.

Still, Tamara didn't put the letter aside. She lay down on her bed, fully dressed, and stared at it again before falling into a dark and dreamless sleep. And it was there when she awoke at six o'clock feeling groggy and out of sorts with a faint headache pressing around her temples. The first thing she saw when she sat up was Rebecca's spiky, graceful handwriting angling across the paper.

'Cool and soothing blues,' Tamara muttered to herself and then shook off the thought. She would die in Calgary; she knew that. It was a cow-town in western Canada made up of Indians, cowboys and oil people. Rebecca had already admitted that the shopping didn't come close to New York stores, the theatre life was minimal and that the city's highest cultural moment was the Calgary Stampede. Tamara had absolutely no intention of burying herself among a lot of provincial hicks; like most New Yorkers, she thought the world ended at the boundaries of the five boroughs.

She didn't eat any dinner, but dressed for a party that night, thinking the canapés her hostess served would save her from eating the last spoonful of peanut butter in the jar in her cupboard. She ignored the queasy, semi-hungry feeling in her stomach and began to forage through her clothes closet. Dressing, for Tamara, was an artistic endeavour. She rarely wore the ordinary and had an eye for unusual combinations, colours or styles that only she could carry off with panache.

Tonight she decided on basic black, putting on

a cocktail number from the 'fifties that she had discovered at a rummage sale. It had a high neck, low back and a slit up the side. She wore patterned black stockings with it and three-inch heels that had a delicate leather fretwork at the toes. Her hair had been brushed until it crackled with static and sat on her shoulders in a thick, carroty-red mass of ripples and crinkly waves. Her eyes were a light blue with darkened lashes, and she outlined their almond shape with mascara.

When she was done, she swivelled before the mirror, thankful that her afternoon nap had erased some of the discoloration beneath her eyes and smoothed out the wrinkles. She was twenty-nine, thin to the point of boniness, and she had an angular face that would never qualify as beautiful. There would be a number of women at the party who would be far prettier, more voluptuous and infinitely sexier than she was, but heads would turn when she entered. Tamara was striking, and she knew how to make the best of what she had.

The party was in a friend's apartment, and the rooms were already crowded and smoke-filled when Tamara arrived. She saw several out-of-work actors and actresses, a retired producer who was trying to make a come-back, a couple of script-writers and almost the entire roll-call of a local avant-garde theatre company. The talk was of New York's theatre world and who had been signed up by a big-name director, who had a decent agent, what auditions were coming up and who was sleeping with whom. The gossip was cynical and sometimes vicious, and Tamara found herself yawning with a combination of tiredness and boredom. She had heard it all many times before; only the names had changed, the situations were always the same.

She munched on a cracker topped with cream cheese and an olive and wandered around the apartment with an unfinished glass of white wine in her hand. She stood at the edge of conversations and chatted idly with acquaintances. She finally came to life when she saw Sheila enter the room, her hand raised in greeting.

'Tam, you look great. Where did you find that dress?'

'Three guesses.'

'Next-to-New, Second-Hand Rose or Recherché.'

'Wrong.'

'It's new? God, did you come into an inheritance or was it on sale?'

'A rummage sale,' Tamara said. 'Where else?'

'Where else,' Sheila echoed. They were old friends, their acquaintance dating back to the days when both were new in New York and naïve about jobs, men and breaking into theatre. Sheila was a lanky blonde who had dreams of being a contralto with the Metropolitan Opera Company. Like Tamara, she juggled lessons and auditions with a job as receptionist for a firm in the garment industry and, like Tamara, she had had only a small success in getting stage roles. She had had several small singing parts in off-off Broadway shows and a couple of revues, but she had been unable to crack a professional opera company. She was, however, one step ahead of Tamara in financial terms. She occasionally received a handout or care package from her indulgent but anxious parents who lived in Minneapolis. Tamara wasn't so fortunate; her parents were divorced and she and her mother hadn't been on speaking terms for more than a year. She would beg, borrow or steal before she would ever ask Martine for help.

'. . . and there's a small place near Columbia,' Sheila was saying. 'We could try it some afternoon.'

Tamara nodded and then asked, 'Are you here alone?'

Sheila gave her an incredulous glance from a pair of long, blue eyes that were her best feature. She had a face that was too narrow to be attractive and a nose that turned up, but she was animated and vivacious, characteristics that off-set her looks. 'Are you kidding? When was the last time you met a decent man in New York?' She waved at the crowds around them. 'They only come in three categories—gay, Mama's boys or they're already attached. Of course I'm alone.'

'What about Tony? I thought you were seeing him.'

'It's over,' Sheila said gloomily.

Tamara gave her a knowing look. 'Which category did he fall in?'

'The third—he was already attached. I just found out he's married and has three kids. Oh, hell, who's kidding whom? I suspected it all along.'

'When did this happen?'

'Over the weekend. I got tired of the old routine, you know, dinner at my place, sex in my bed and then Mr Wonderful leaves at midnight like Cinderella. When I insisted on knowing where he was going, the truth poured out. Of course, his wife doesn't understand him . . .'

'. . . and they haven't slept together in months,' Tamara added, 'and the kids are bleeding him dry and he's lonely and sensitive and miserable.'

Sheila laughed. 'You've heard it all.'

'I gave up on married men years ago,' replied Tamara, hiding a yawn behind her hand. 'They all sound the same after a while.'

'Well, he was gorgeous,' Sheila said with nostalgia, 'and he always brought me flowers.' She sighed and then went on, 'So, what's new with you? Did you try that new play at the Atheneum Theater?'

'I didn't get the part.'

'Oh, Tam, I'm sorry. I knew you wanted it.'

Tamara shrugged unhappily. 'Sometimes I wonder if I'll ever make it.'

'Sure you will. We both will. It's just a matter of getting that lucky break.'

Tamara looked at the gleam in Sheila's eyes and knew that there was no use in questioning that hopeful logic or arguing that maybe the lucky break would never come, that maybe she and Sheila and all the other would-be actresses and singers might never make it beyond the round of auditions and their unfulfilled dreams. It was a thought that had occurred to her recently with greater and greater frequency, but she had attributed it to her exhaustion. She wasn't used to thinking about her life in such a negative way. Tamara knew she was good; she knew that if she only could get the chance to prove just how good an actress she was, the world would sit up and take notice. It was that confidence and ambition that had kept her going for years, pinching pennies, struggling just above the subsistence level and constantly taking classes so that when the break came she would be waiting and prepared.

Still, there were times when she felt as if her dream of success was as elusive as a will-o'-the-wisp, beckoning to her to come closer and then fading whenever she drew near. She was so tired of the waiting and the scheming, the hopes that rose up only to be shattered once again, the constant erosion of a wish that had once burned within her, its force allowing her to break free of Martine and survive in the wilderness that was Manhattan. The fire of her ambition was still hot and she prayed passionately for that one moment when a producer or director would see her for what she was, but a part of Tamara felt as if the flame had, perhaps, burned too close to the quick of her. Like ash, her dream was growing more and more insubstantial. She could no longer hold on to it and grasp it as if it were a living thing; vital and warming and real.

'. . . and I heard,' Sheila had gone on to say,

'that there might be a walk-on part at the Metropolitan, so I'm planning to go tomorrow and beat down the doors. Even a walk-on is better than nothing.'

Tamara nodded and then launched into her appeal. 'Sheila, do you have any extra cash this month? I'm sort of low.' It wasn't an unusual request, and she knew Sheila wouldn't be upset by it. They had often helped one another out with loans.

'Oh, Tam, I'm sorry, but I didn't tell you. I've decided to change apartments, and I just performed surgery on my bank account for a security deposit on a new one. I was so sick of living with cockroaches, and remember that couple next door? They fight all the time, morning, afternoon, midnight. I'm not getting any sleep. Anyway, I found a great place in the West End and I . . .'

Tamara smiled and nodded and acted as if it didn't matter that Sheila couldn't even lend her a dime. Inside her head, however, she was calculating madly, wondering if she could get by on one meal a day, eating only at the restaurant where she waitressed at night. The boss there wasn't like Mr Freiberg; he was stingy with food for the help, but if she scrounged a bit, perhaps she could manage. Oh, she knew that it would be far more rational if she quit the jazz class, but she loved it so much; the heavy beat of the music and the chance it gave her to move her body in those sensuous rhythms. Besides, everyone knew how much easier it was to get a stage job if you could dance. And, of course, she didn't need the Persian lamb, but it would make such a great addition to her wardrobe. Tamara sighed and resigned herself to one meal a day.

Sheila went off after that to talk to another friend, and Tamara moved around the apartment again. Someone had dimmed the lights and put on a record of calypso music. In the living room, several couples were dancing, and the atmosphere was smoky from too many cigarettes and not enough ventilation. She felt another bout of dizziness come on and stepped out of the apartment into the hallway, leaning against the wall and taking a deep breath. She didn't notice the man standing near by until he spoke.

'Hot in there, isn't it?'

He was an older man, in his fifties, Tamara guessed, dark and heavyset. He was dressed more conservatively than the rest of the crowd at the party in a grey three-piece suit and a blue tie. His dark hair had silver strands in it, and he wasn't, she noticed, wearing a wedding ring although he sported, on his little finger, a gold ring with an obsidian stone.

'Yes,' she said, 'it is.'

'Friend of the host?' he asked.

'The hostess. We take an acting class together.'

'Ah—so you're an actress.' Dark eyes swept over her, taking in the sophisticated black dress, the heavy mass of red hair. 'Have I seen you in anything?'

'Do you go off-off Broadway?'

He shook his head. 'Sorry.'

'Well, I was in one of those shows where
there's no scenery and the actors have to disrobe
half-way through to prove the avant-garde sensi-
bilities of the playwright.'

'And did you?'

'Did I what?'

'Disrobe.'

Tamara shook her head. 'The theatre was like a
barn, and it had more draughts than a beer joint.'

He stared at her for a moment, not getting her
pun for a while, and then he laughed. 'Martin
Patterson,' he said, introducing himself, 'and
you're . . . ?'

'Tamara Clark.'

'Want to,' he gestured towards the door beside
her and the noise emanating out of it, 'split?'

Tamara assessed him coolly, wondered if the
absence of a wedding ring was deliberate, judged
that he had money from the cut of his suit and
decided that he was more attractive on second
notice than on the first. Besides, he was different
from most of the men with whom she went out.
Her last few boy-friends had been theatre people,
hopefuls like herself. She thought that maybe
Martin Patterson might prove to be refreshing
and gave a slight shrug. 'Sure,' she said.

He took her to dinner at a small elegant restaurant where the tables were set with real linen
and the flickering of candles provided an atmosphere of intimacy. Tamara discovered that she
was starving and ate, not only at her entrée, a
Coquille St Jacques, but part of Martin's as well.
He sat back and watched her with a small smile

curving his lips. They talked about theatre, living in Manhattan and his job. Martin, as it turned out, was divorced, a stockbroker and into books. He had a vast collection of first editions, signed by their authors, and antiquarian titles.

Tamara listened to him talk, and mentally debated the pros and cons of going to bed with him. He was older, staid and conservative; on the other hand, he was definitely looking for a bed partner. She knew men well enough to sense that this expensive, luxurious dinner wasn't going to come free of charge. He had been watching her with the predatory air of a hunter who has a bird with exotic plumage in his sights. She wondered if he were the type of man who was old-fashioned enough to want a 'mistress' with all the trimmings or whether he was interested in something quick and fast with no strings attached.

Tamara knew she was cynical about men, but she hadn't any reason to be otherwise. She had been used and abused too often not to have developed a shield around her heart and her sentiments. She saw the nebulous terrain between men and women as the site for intense jungle-type warfare where any weapon or tactic was legitimate and only the stealthy survived. The world she envisioned was rapacious, calculating and sometimes frightening, but it was the only one she knew. Her early naïvety had been replaced by the street sense that comes from hard experiences; her caring about others had yielded to disdain. There was a toughness to Tamara, the result of many wounds and a scarred soul.

Tamara had often wished that she could live without men, but neither isolation nor celibacy suited her. It wasn't that she liked sex so much; the act itself was rarely satisfying for her. It was the loneliness that got to her; her empty apartment, sleeping by herself, waking up to a day without a human touch. It was the warmth of men's arms that Tamara sought, those embraces that enclosed her in a secure circle and that, no matter how brief or careless they might be, gave her the sensation of affection, of caring, of love. She hadn't yet come to the realisation that these empty embraces only left her hungrier for more. In fact, Tamara had never actually been introspective enough to wonder why she slept with so many men or why each affair was so short and unfulfilling. To a friend like Sheila, she would laugh off her motives as mercenary or lustful; to herself she merely thought of her succession of men as the way the modern world worked. Relationships were transitory; men were fickle; and the important thing was to survive. And if survival meant warding off the demons of loneliness then Tamara was for it. She only knew, as she knew tonight, that she didn't want to go home alone.

So when Martin asked her back to his place, she went. As she had expected, he had money, and his apartment was furnished well and tastefully with winged chairs and a large, dark sofa. His valuable collection of books stood along one wall, and he spent some time pointing out the best of it to her. She wondered as she watched him finger the covers and pages of the books whether he got more of a sexual kick out of paper than he would out of her. He talked about the books the way some men talked about women.

'. . . and this one,' he was saying, 'is a real beauty.' His fingers, thick but neatly manicured, lovingly caressed its spine and the leather cover with its gold binding. 'A Dickens first edition.'

'It's nice,' she murmured.

'I paid a fortune for it, but it was worth it. Dickens is my speciality.'

Tamara tried to smile, but a nausea was rising in her, an uneasy mass pressing against the back of her tongue. She felt as if she had eaten far too much of rich, heavy food, and her stomach was rebelling against the sudden gorging she had done in the restaurant. Her tiredness was also returning; her legs had started to tremble and a yawn kept threatening to break through her fixed smile. The thought of going to bed with Martin Patterson was becoming less and less appealing.

'How about a drink?' he offered. 'A little cognac or whisky or perhaps you'd like something sweeter, like Kahlua?'

Tamara felt herself grow pale. 'Nothing, thanks.'

He walked over to an oak buffet that held a cut-glass decanter and several glasses. 'You're very quiet,' he said. 'Somehow you didn't strike me as that type.'

Her smile was sickly; her skin had broken out in a sweat and she felt horribly clammy and cold. 'I'm not; I'm usually . . .' Tamara never finished her sentence. She gagged, feeling her dinner surge up within her. She covered her mouth with her hand, and ran to the bathroom, barely making it in time. She vomited copiously and, afterwards, when her stomach was finally empty and the retching was over, she sat on the floor and leaned against the wall with her eyes closed, her whole body still shaking.

'Hey, are you okay?'

It was Martin, standing in the doorway, looking down at her. Tamara understood why he wore a faint expression of distaste. The bathroom still had a sour odour, and the fluorescent lights brought out the worst of her pale complexion and orangey hair. Poor man, she thought, as she struggled to her feet. He had anticipated a pleasant evening topped by an exciting, sexual interlude; instead, he had a sick woman on his hands, one who couldn't stop trembling and whose sex appeal had tumbled to nothing.

'I . . . think I'd better go home,' she mumbled.

His voice was eager, too eager. 'Yes,' he said. 'I'll come down with you and get you a cab.'

Tamara peered into the mirror over the vanity and pushed back damp tendrils of hair that clung to her forehead. She felt weak, still dizzy and utterly drained. All she wanted to do was go back to her own apartment, crawl into bed and die. This need drove her to say, 'I don't have enough money to take a cab.'

He was already delving into his pockets. 'Here's a ten,' he offered, peeling a bill off a tight wad. 'That should do it.'

The ten paid the cabby's fare and still left her with four dollars which was enough, Tamara estimated, to buy some breakfast in the morning —if she felt like eating, that was. Her apartment had never looked as bleak or as desolate as it did in the dark hours of the morning when the sky was blackest and the lamplight made everything look stark and unreal, like a stage setting without actors. The bed was rumpled from her afternoon nap; the clothes she had worn that day were tossed over a chair; her dresser held uncapped bottles of cosmetics. An opened lipstick had rolled right to the edge of the night-table, its orange bright and garish against the dark, chipped wood. Everything in Tamara's apartment had either been lent by friends or salvaged from second-hand furniture stores. As she looked around her, she was struck by the ugliness of her room. She had never noticed just how bad it was; she had never seen that the colours within it clashed, that the green of the curtains didn't match the worn-out print in the old Persian carpet, or that the bedstead and dresser were clunky and graceless. Most women cared about their living environment; Tamara had never given a damn before.

Despite her exhaustion, sleep didn't come to her easily. Her mind whirled with money problems; her memory kept replaying the evening with Martin Patterson. She remembered the distaste on his face and his eagerness to get rid of her. If he had been a friend, he would have comforted her, perhaps even taken care of her.

But he was neither a friend nor an acquaintance. He was a stranger with whom she planned to be intimate, a man that she would sleep with because his company and his body could fill in the emptiness at the core of her.

Wasn't that ugly, too? she thought as she turned and twisted, the nausea still tightening her stomach in spasms. Wasn't it exceedingly ugly that she was so desperate for human contact that she would use anyone to satisfy that need? Tamara had never seen her one-night stands or brief affairs from that angle before, and it gave her a frightening and uneasy feeling. She had always thought of casual sex as moments of mutual pleasure without the complications of personality, opinions and commitment.

She slept finally, but not for long. She awoke around six o'clock, feeling as if she hadn't rested at all. Her stomach was still queasy and she wasn't sure she would have the energy to get up and attend the classes scheduled that day. It occurred to Tamara at that point that she might be seriously ill; that perhaps the tiredness and dizziness and nausea were not from overwork or a viral infection, but were from some disease far more dangerous. She thought about going to a doctor and then wondered how she would pay for his services and medication if she were sick. She had no medical insurance and she had never applied for Medicaid. Just the thought of going through reams of red tape to prove she was indigent made Tamara feel even more tired than she already was.

But she struggled to sit up and curled against the headboard, pulling the blankets around her and feeling sick and depressed. What at night had looked bleak and stagelike, in daylight had a different appearance. The carpet was threadbare, one of the chairs had stuffing coming out of its seat and there were cracks in the plaster of each wall. And she matched, Tamara thought sadly, looking down at her wrists where the sleeves of her nightgown were frayed and then to the edge of the sheet with its torn edges and small holes. Her room was shabby and so was she. Her clothes closet was full of other people's hand-me-downs and discards; nothing she owned was new or bright and shiny. Every object had the dejected, drooping look of something that had been used too often or seen better days.

Oh, she was able to cover up her shabbiness by being animated and charming, by using clever little accessories like colourful scarfs and the right belts, but the reality was there all the same and anyone who looked closely would see the tell-tale marks; altered seams, hems worn shiny from use, shoes whose scuff marks were barely hidden beneath the polish. Tamara had never minded before; to her, it had all been a game she was playing until her big break came and the dollars would flow in like manna from heaven in quantities so extraordinary that she would never have to worry about money again. Until her big break came . . .

Her glance lingered on her hands clutching the sheet and then fell on Rebecca's letter which had

ended up on the floor beside her bed. For a
moment, she was tugged by it and by the comfort
and solace it offered; a place to stay that was
gracious and attractive, the ministrations of a
sister who liked to take care of people, three
square meals a day that wouldn't cost her a cent,
and hours of time that wouldn't be taken up by a
frenzied rushing from class to audition to work.
Peace, that's what Rebecca had offered her, and
then Tamara made a grimace. Boredom, she
thought, excruciatingly painful boredom. She
would love to see her nephew and new niece, and
she always enjoyed being with Rebecca, but what
about the rest of it when the novelty wore off, and
she would have to face hours of nothing to do
in Calgary? She could see herself, sitting by a
window and watching the wind pass through
the tall, brown prairie grasses; that endless and
monotonous motion.

Her stomach lurched and Tamara tried to swal-
low, thinking oh, no, not again. She couldn't bear
the idea of being sick again, and she closed her
eyes, trying to will away the nausea. She prayed
to a God she barely believed in, asking for him to
please, please make her feel better, and she
curled up even tighter against the pillows, a small
thin figure in the expanse of tumbled sheets, her
face a stark white against the vibrant red of her
hair. Her eyes were closed tightly in an attempt to
ward off dizziness, and she didn't even open
them when the phone rang. She merely reached
out, grabbed it before the world spun around her
and sank down into bed with the receiver against

her ear. The rest of the phone tumbled on to the floor with a bang and a clatter.

'Tamara, is that you? What's all that noise?'

She had been hot and sweaty before, but now she felt icy. It was amazing how Martine could have that effect on her. 'The phone dropped,' she said.

Her mother's voice was smooth. 'I haven't heard from you in so long, I thought I'd phone.'

'We haven't been on speaking terms. Remember?'

'Darling, I've never felt that way. I don't believe in that sort of thing. It's destructive.'

If Tamara hadn't felt so ill, she would have laughed. 'That's profound,' she replied.

'Why must you be so antagonistic?'

'I was born that way.'

'You were a *lovely* child.'

Even in her weakened state, Tamara had the resources to attack. 'It takes a while for some *inherited* characteristics to reveal themselves.'

Martine's voice was frigid. 'I didn't phone you to argue.'

I'll bet, Tamara thought. 'And why did you phone?' she asked wearily.

'I'd like you to come to dinner. We haven't seen you in months. Celia was wondering about you.'

It was typical of Martine, Tamara thought bitterly, to use her younger sister to make her feel guilty. It was true that she hadn't seen Celia in months and it was also true that, no matter how much enmity she bore to Martine, she was inflicting her anger on an innocent, but even these truths could not persuade Tamara to see her mother.

'Tell her I'm fine,' she said.

'You mean you won't come to dinner?'

'I . . .' Tamara knew that she had the choice of either hanging up and having Martine phone her again or show up at her apartment, or she could try to put her mother off with a vague excuse that would just result in another vicious round of battles. The thought of seeing Martine in person made her go limp. She was far too exhausted to have a confrontation or another major battle, but Tamara knew how persistent and nagging Martine could be, particularly when she was ordering a command performance. Tamara wondered if Martine had planned to have other guests to dinner and had decided, with that peculiar logic of hers, that she would like to show off her daughter, the New York actress. Of course, when she did that, her voice would have a snide, malicious undertone to it that would let Tamara know just how insincere she was. It was the type of thing for which Martine had a wonderful skill—making Tamara feel even more like a failure than she already was.

Tamara shifted in bed so that she was lying on her side and opened her eyes. The room swayed a bit in a sickening way and then settled into its usual dimension. Her glance, once more, fell to the floor, and she saw salvation lying there, pure and simple and sweet. 'I can't,' she said.

'I haven't even told you the date,' returned Martine coldly.

'I'm going to visit Rebecca,' Tamara said. Relief swept through her like a warm, soothing wave, and the icy trembling that had come over her when she heard Martine's voice eased.

She hadn't known how much she had fought using the escape offered to her until the fight was no longer there, leaving her emptied and serene? What did the boredom matter, the lousy shopping, the cultural wasteland, when Rebecca would be there to help her; to offer her love and caring and compassion? And, for a time, she wouldn't be lonely any more and driven into the arms of men who saw her only as an object to be used and then discarded. Tamara knew she was being selfish, but then Martine had always forced her to intense heights of selfishness. It had been the only way she knew to survive.

'And I'm flying to Calgary,' she went on.

'There's still time to . . .'

Tamara smiled and simply embellished the truth with a small, white lie. 'My flight,' she said, 'leaves tonight.'

CHAPTER TWO

'So you think the Stampeders have a chance at the Grey Cup?'

Jake shrugged as the bartender wiped the counter in front of him. He wasn't a football freak, but he was knowledgeable enough to engage in the common male pastime of game analysis. 'You can't tell.'

'That's what I say,' the bartender agreed. 'I'm not one of those armchair prophets.'

'I'd hate to see Toronto win.'

'Yeah.' The bartender looked at him expectantly. 'Want a fill up?'

Jake shook his head. 'No thanks.' He glanced at his watch and grimaced.

'Waiting for a plane?'

'From New York. It's over two hours late.'

'Ever been there?'

'Nope.'

The bartender leaned against the counter and looked reminiscent. There was no one else in the bar except for Jake, and he had time on his hands. 'I went there back in '75. Couldn't take it.'

'No?'

'It's noisy and dirty . . . and the people are something else.'

'Why?'

'They don't give you the time of day. They're arrogant, that's what I say.'

'I've heard that,' Jake nodded, 'but I suppose it's the crowd mentality. Individually they're probably just like anyone else.'

The bartender hitched up his sleeve. 'Could be. Are you waiting for a friend?'

'A friend's sister-in-law.' Jake stood up and put on his white stetson. 'He couldn't make it so I got the job.'

'She's been to Calgary before?'

Jake shook his head. 'It's her first.'

'So you don't know her from a hole in the wall.'

'Right,' Jake said. 'This is strictly a mercy mission.'

The bartender began to wipe down the spigots at the edge of the counter. 'And how late did you say the plane was?'

'Two hours.' Jake shrugged his shoulders into his suede jacket.

The bartender gave a small whistle. 'I hope your pal appreciates it.'

'I don't mind,' Jake said, digging a couple of dollars out of his wallet and putting the money down on the bar. 'He's done plenty for me.'

Jake wandered down to the waiting-room, idly reading the signs and posters on the wall and letting his earlier impatience die away. He didn't like wasting time, but he didn't begrudge the fact that Rebecca hadn't been able to come to the airport to pick up Tamara. It wasn't her fault that

Guy was out of town and the baby's colic had got
so bad so fast that she had had to bring her to the
hospital. Even he had felt stomach pangs when
he had stopped at the house and listened to little
Jennifer scream.

No, he didn't mind helping Rebecca out; she
was Guy's wife and Guy was special. He had
been Jake's high school and college pal and still
was his business partner and closest friend. Cordelia and Franklin McLaren, Guy's parents, had
been a surrogate family for Jake when he had
wanted to escape his own, and he still visited
Cordelia regularly, especially now that she was a
widow. Jake had always felt that he owed the
McLarens a lot. He had grown up with no mother
and a drunk for a father, a combination that
would have sent most adolescent kids into drugs
or alcohol or worse. But Guy and his family had
been a steadying influence and one, Jake believed, that had saved him from becoming a
juvenile delinquent.

He had certainly had the sort of compulsions
that could have got him in trouble with the law.
As a teenager, he had hated school, loved fast
cars, and had been excited by the idea of danger.
There was no softening maternal influence to
check him, and he couldn't bear staying at home
and watching his father drink himself into an
oblivion. At first, he had been a loner, staying
away from other kids so that they wouldn't know
the shame of his family, but when he reached
fifteen, gang behaviour attracted him. He began
to spend hours lounging around shopping malls

and discovered that there were a thousand and one temptations open to a kid who didn't think the world gave a damn about him.

Since the boys that Jake hung out with hated any form of activity that smacked of adult intervention, they were restless with an energy that had no decent or legal outlet. They were vandals and troublemakers; some were shop-lifters and the head of the gang, a wiry boy with a broken front tooth, a hooked nose and the beginnings of acne, had been caught trying to steal a car. Jake admired his swagger and his nonchalance, tried to imitate him and, despite an essential goodness in his own nature, was fatally attracted to the destructive attitude of the gang members. He was, he understood later, heading down a road that would have ultimately led to arrest and jail when Guy entered his life.

He had been at the ice-skating rink, fooling around with a hockey stick and puck with a bunch of the other boys. They were all dressed in jeans, ski jackets and heavy mitts. Despite the chill in the air none of them was wearing a hat. Jake, who had just turned fifteen, was tall, lanky and still unbearded. He had not yet developed the heavy musculature that would characterise him as an adult, and he appeared almost fragile, his blond hair falling over his forehead, his dark eyes fringed by long black lashes. He had a face that was inherently sweet but often marred by a scowl and a frown. He liked to jam his hands in his pockets, hunch his shoulders and watch people from the corners of his eyes. He wanted to act like a man, but he wasn't precisely sure how to go about it.

His friends on the rink were being rough, sending the puck back and forth with a vicious speed and banging into one another in imitation of the violence of professional players. The air around them was filled with swear words that graphically described the act of love in the most obscene terms. Jake noticed that some of the adults near by blanched, but he shrugged and ignored their reaction. He had realised long ago that the act of swearing held a lot of satisfactions. It let off steam and it annoyed the hell out of other people; he indulged in it frequently and with great pleasure.

The game grew rougher and faster despite the fact that there were other people who were using the rink. Jake figured that eventually someone would come along and throw them off the ice, but until then it was a free world. He jostled a kid next to him and sent the puck singing along the ice. It smacked into another boy's stick and flew in the air, hitting a small child who had just stepped into the rink—a little girl wearing a turquoise toque over her blonde curls and a matching skating skirt. It hit her in the shoulder, knocking her down against the boards. Jake didn't think she was hurt badly—she was wearing a thick jacket —but she was only about six years old and she began to cry.

What Jake's friends did next was typical. Since it was against their unspoken adolescent code to express emotions in a normal manner or to show remorse to the outside world, they took their feelings out on one another in the only way that was acceptable.

The kid whose stick the puck had last hit was punched in the shoulder. 'You jerk,' someone said.

'You—' someone else shouted.

They banged into one another, cuffed each other in the head and were generally noisy and obtrusive. No one went near the little girl to offer her comfort; that sentimental gesture would have undermined the group's belief in their burgeoning manhood and, when the little girl's father rushed past them, his face angry, his voice berating them for their carelessness, there was a collective turning of ill will in his direction. Given the chance, Jake's friends would always take out their feelings of embarrassment and shame on the adult world. It was so much easier to do than turning that angry, unhappy eye in on themselves and seeing the flaws that lay within.

'You kids shouldn't be fooling around on this rink,' he shouted at them. 'There are little children here.'

'Go to hell,' one of the boys yelled, and some of the others jeered and whistled.

Jake neither joined in nor objected. He skated unobtrusively to one side and banged his hockey stick against the boards. He was rarely an instigator in a group situation although he would join in if forced to, if he noticed one of the other boys eyeing him or if he were challenged. But it wasn't in his nature to be mean or nasty and, deep down, he was often bothered by things the other kids did and said. He never admitted this to anyone and only rarely to himself. It was far safer to simply move with the crowd, use the constant noise and conversation to fill the empty spaces in his head and buttress his own insecurities with the protection of numbers. Although he would never have hinted of his reluctance to a soul, he didn't like to fight. The restlessness and destructive anger of the group buffeted him only now and then. He preferred to stay on the edge of things and watch—like now, when the father was rushing towards his daughter at one end of the rink and his friends were circling around the other, using their hockey sticks as if they were swords and trying to trip one another up.

The girl's father didn't make it to her first. It was a boy who arrived at her side and helped her stand up, a tall boy of about Jake's age with dark hair, dressed in a blue ski jacket, who moved easily on his skates and was gentle as he brushed the tears off the girl's face with his gloved hand. The girl, wobbly on her own skates, clung to his leg as she tried to stay upright, and the boy laid a steadying hand on her head. Then he turned and looked towards the other end of the rink at the gang, and his gaze was intercepted by Jake who stopped his restless banging against the boards and the ceaseless shifting of his skates. The look spoke of dislike and disgust; it was adult, mature and unsettling in a face that young. The look made Jake want to hide. It was one thing to have an adult censuring him, but it was quite another to have a boy his own age look at him as if he were an animal.

The other boy didn't look afraid either; he didn't seem to care that his look accused Jake's friends, a clear and unmistakable challenge of their activities and behaviour. He was a hand-some boy with strong features, dark eyes, and broad shoulders beneath his ski jacket. He was the kind of boy that sent Jake's friends into a frenzy of fury; he represented everything they were not. Just by looking at him Jake could tell that he had nice parents, a home with comfort in it and that confidence that comes from the knowledge that one belongs. Jake felt a lump grow in his throat, an unmanly lump of tears and misery that he swallowed with difficulty.

'Who is that creep?' one of his friends said as he skated by, and then yelled as he swept down the ice. 'Hey, creep!'

But the other boy didn't seem to care. He was talking to the little girl's father, and Jake could see their smiles, the giving of thanks and the acknowledgement. Then the boy skated out on to the ice, and Jake could sense the gathering of his friends and the cumulative power of their malice. He didn't know what they planned to do; they were still skating around one another in seeming-ly erratic patterns, but there were smiles on their faces that hinted at something formal and orga-nised and dangerous. Jake quickly looked at the boy who was now skating backwards, his blades scraping one after the other on the ice. That action took Jake's breath away. How could he turn his back that way? Couldn't he feel the waves of hatred coming at him across the ice?

The head of the gang was whispering to someone and there was a small nod as if to say yes, let's go, and then Jake did the unexpected. He hadn't known he was going to move until he felt the ice sliding beneath him. He hadn't a clear idea of why he was skating towards that other boy and away from the friends that had protected him. His emotions were complex and muddled and confusing. He didn't hate the other boy; in fact, he admired his courage. He didn't even know him, but he didn't want him to get hurt. It didn't seem fair that an act of kindness and generosity should be punished by violence.

But he was trembling as he crossed the space of ice that separated his friends from the boy who was skating so nonchalantly backwards. He felt the cold breeze of isolation on the back of his neck, the eyes of the others watching him. They called to him, 'Hey, Jake, where you going?' And he heard a derisive whistle. But he couldn't stop. That clear and condemning look had touched something deep in Jake; a chord of humanity that he had been forced to suppress, a shame that he could bear no longer. He was only dimly aware of the fact that he had recognised in the other boy the true essence of masculinity and had understood that it didn't come from swagger or lying or the ability to speak dirty words. It came from gentleness, from sensitivity, from the willingness to care.

He skated beside the other boy and fell into his

pattern so that they were both moving together, backwards and in a large circle. 'Hey, you,' he said, 'you'd better get off the ice.'

The other boy looked at him. 'Why?'

'Because of them.' Jake jerked his head backwards to indicate the crowd of boys at the other end of the rink.

'You've got nice friends.'

'Hey, I'm just trying to warn you!'

The boy was smiling. 'Why?' he asked again.

Jake was stunned by that smile. It refuted everything that the gang thought about the boys who went straight, got good grades, mowed their parents' lawns and were decent and respectable. There was a bravery in that smile and something devil-may-care as if the other boy was looking forward to the fight.

'They'll kill you,' he said.

The other boy shrugged.

'Hey, man, it's six to one!'

'Five to two,' the other boy corrected him with a grin, 'unless you decide to change sides.'

When the violence came, it was as brief and as intense as a squall; there were too many adults around to allow for a free-for-all. Jake was suddenly buffeted from two sides and shoved into the boards while someone growled in his ear, 'Traitor!' He felt a wave of pain in his shoulder as he hit the wood, and he tried desperately to swing around fast enough so that he could score a hit himself. He did manage to punch someone's middle and hear a groan that gave him great satisfaction but, within seconds, the other boys were gone as quickly as they had come, skating across the ice to the gate, yelling obscenities as they went. Jake slumped against the boards, feeling the adrenalin of the fight seeping out of him as the pain in his shoulder increased and the realisation of his outcast status came over him.

'Not bad,' a voice near him said and Jake turned to see the other boy grinning from ear to ear, one hand covering his eye.

'What do you mean—not bad?'

The boy was pointing at the ice where small drops of blood were dotting the surface red. 'I got one of them in the nose.'

'Yeah,' Jake agreed, smiling. 'I guess you did.' He hoped it was the leader of the gang who had copped it; he suddenly fiercely hoped that that hook of a nose had been ground to mush on his ugly mug.

The other boy dropped his hand from his face, revealing the beginnings of a black eye, and held it out to Jake. 'I'm Guy,' he announced solemnly. 'Guy McLaren.'

Jake pulled off his glove, took the proferred hand in his and shook it with a matching formality. 'Jake,' he said. 'Jake DeBlais.'

Their friendship had been cemented on that handshake and the sharing of injuries. Jake had ended up with a cracked collar-bone, and Guy had an eye that went every colour of the rainbow and was swollen shut for a week. Guy had taken Jake home with him, and Cordelia had fussed over them, driven them to the hospital and then brought them back again. She had wanted to bring Jake to his house, but he had shaken his head, mumbled something about his father not being around and, after a shrewd glance at him, Cordelia had placed her lips together and set him up in the other bed in Guy's room. For the first time in his short life, Jake discovered what it was like to be mothered.

He loved it; he drank in the warmth and comforting like an animal that had been dying of thirst. He was the best patient Cordelia had ever had. Guy complained about his eye, refused bowls of his mother's famous chicken soup and was willing to be waited on hand and foot. Jake, on the other hand, didn't take anything for granted. He ate and drank everything Cordelia set before him, he tried his hardest to dress himself on his own, and he smiled whenever she was around. Cordelia confided in her husband, Franklin, that Jake was the 'sweetest boy' she had ever seen and that something should be done about that father of his. Jake was past caring that someone else had learned the truth about his family. Earlier, he would have cringed at the thought of baring his soul to any of his friends and much less an adult, but he had had a long talk with Cordelia about the mother who had walked out of the house when he was two years old and a father who went on frequent and disgusting drinking binges. There was something about the way Cordelia took the news, her head tilted to one side, her expression sympathetic but practical, that let Jake know he was in good hands.

Cordelia was a small person with a massive amount of energy; Franklin was a large and silent man who smiled often. Jake couldn't understand it at first—why Franklin always smiled at him. His own father rarely smiled except when he was on a laughing jag after he had downed a bottle of gin. He would laugh about any stupid thing until the laughter in him wound down like an uncoiled spring. Then, nothing seemed funny to him any more, and he would either cry or hit Jake or fall asleep on the floor. It was a pattern that had a depressing regularity to it, and Jake had learned to stay out of the way when his father was drinking. It was safer, he had found, to hide out in his room or leave the house than stick around and try to help a man who didn't want to be helped. He had been slapped around far too often.

So Franklin's smile upset Jake at first. He hadn't known where it came from; it had taken him a while to realise that Franklin was a happy man with a good law practice, a devoted wife and a son he could be proud of. Happiness wasn't an emotion that Jake was familiar with and, for a long time after he had met Guy, he would watch the McLarens carefully to see if their façade was real or whether it would crack and reveal something darker inside. It wasn't that the family was perfect or even-tempered all the time; he had seen Cordelia get furious at Guy and he had heard Guy complain about his parents, but there was an underlying core of security and contentment among them that made tempers cool quickly and any outburst end with smiles.

Once Jake's collar had healed a bit, he had gone home. The house was bleak when he returned, and he felt that familiar curl of misery set in. The McLarens' house had been bright and cheerful with large, comfortable pieces of furniture; his own showed that no one gave a damn about it. Neglect was in the cracked paint on the outside and the dingy walls on the inside, in the old pieces of furniture with faded colours and worn threads. Dustballs floated in corners and there was a layer of grime in the bathroom and kitchen. Occasionally Jake or his father tried to clean the house, but their sporadic efforts were never very effective. When Jake pushed open the door, walked in and saw the newspapers scattered in the living room, the full ashtrays and empty bottles littering the table, his hatred of his father rose within him like bile.

Sam was standing in the doorway of the kitchen, wearing baggy jeans, a dirty T-shirt and he hadn't shaved that morning. He was a big man, as big as Jake would be one day, but his muscles had gone soft and his belly hung out over the buckle of his belt. He had also been good-looking once, but drink had blurred his features and thickened them. A spray of broken capillaries coloured one cheek pink.

'Hello, boy,' he said.

Jake swallowed. 'Hi, Dad.' He wondered if Sam had missed work that day or whether he had managed to drive his run. He delivered bread for a local bakery; it was his fifth job in two years. Finances were always a touchy subject in the

DeBlais household despite the fact that they paid almost nothing for the house. It had belonged to Sam's parents and had no mortgage. But most of Sam's wages went on booze, cigarettes and an occasional woman.

'What did you do to your arm?' He pointed at the sling.

'I told you when I phoned. I broke my collar-bone.'

'Oh, yeah,' Sam mumbled. 'Yeah, you did. Who were those people?'

'I met a guy at the rink. We're friends now.'

'Friends, hey?'

From experience, he recognised the pattern of his father's drinking. The early glow of camaraderie and good cheer had faded and all the signs of the next stage had set in. Sam was becoming morose and abusive, and Jake spoke warily. 'He's a nice guy. And his mother took care of me.'

'Now, isn't that sweet.' His father stepped forward, and Jake suddenly got a whiff of alcohol and stale cigarettes and sweat. He gagged a bit and Sam added, 'Miss your mother, do you?'

Jake began to inch to one side, towards the staircase. 'No,' he said, 'I don't.'

'You shouldn't miss her. She was a bitch.'

'Yeah, you told me that.' A bitch—a pretty woman with dark, flowing hair and a slender figure. Jake had seen pictures of her in an old album up in the attic. She had laughed at him from the pages, carefree and happy, standing next to his father who had been unrecognisable: handsome, debonair in a dark suit, his hair slicked back in the style of the 'forties. Jake had never understood what had happened to that couple; they seemed godlike in the photos, untouchable, immune from worry and misfortune. Sometimes, he liked to imagine that the two people in the photograph were his parents now, and that they laughed together, the three of them, while they were riding in a car or having breakfast in a shiny, bright kitchen.

'She didn't want you. Did I tell you that?'

Hurriedly. 'Yeah.'

'That's why she left me, boy. I know that's why she left me.'

Another step closer to the stairs. 'Sure, Dad, that must have been why.'

Sam was closer now. 'You think I'm a failure, don't you?'

'No.'

'You think I like being judged by you, you little creep? You think I like seeing you watch me like that—the way your mother did?'

'No.'

Sam reached for him. 'So stop staring at me!' Jake just managed to slip under his arm and up the stairs. 'Come back here!'

But Jake was running up the stairs two steps at a time, running as hard and as fast as he could, his breath coming quickly in his chest, heart pounding like crazy. He knew what would happen if his father got hold of him; he would be slapped on the side of the head or thrown against a wall or his good shoulder held in a grip so tight he would have bruises for days afterwards.

'Come back!'

He heard his father head up the stairs after him and then the stumble, the loud curse and, just as he slipped in the door and shut it behind him, the sound of Sam's heavy footsteps going back into the kitchen. Jake leaned against the wall of his bedroom and closed his eyes, panting. The pain in his injured collar-bone flared up again and throbbed in his shoulder. He stood there for a while, as rigid and immobile as a statue, waiting for his frightened heartbeat to subside and praying that Sam wouldn't change his mind. The lock of his door was broken; his father had torn it off the wall a month ago.

Images filled the blank space behind his closed eyelids. Jake tried not to see them, but he couldn't help it. He didn't want to remember the pillow with the crewel-work that sat at an angle on the big winged chair in the McLarens' living room. He wanted to forget watching the way Cordelia had sipped at a soup she was cooking, and the paper moustache Guy had taped to a photograph of his father that stood on the mantel above the fireplace. That was stupid stuff, little details that no one but someone as dumb as himself cared or thought about much. Who gave a damn about pillows or the way Mrs McLaren had tasted her soup or if that phony moustache made Mr McLaren look foolish? Who gave a damn anyway? Why couldn't he just forget it?

Jake opened his eyes and tried to look at the wall where he had pinned up pictures of his favourite hockey stars; especially Maurice 'The

Rocket' Richard, but he couldn't see them. Tears blocked his vision, blurred the faces on the poster and made the world seem misty and trembling. Hating himself for the weakness of crying, Jake rubbed furiously at his eyes, but he couldn't stop the tears from flowing. He didn't want to make a sound; he didn't want to give Sam the satisfaction of knowing that he had broken him down. So Jake crouched against the wall and cried silently, the tears wetting his eyelashes, running down his cheeks and dripping, one by one, on to the white sling that held up his arm.

Of course, he had grown up since then, and Jake couldn't remember the last time he had cried. Guy had become his best friend, and he had spent all the time that he could at the McLaren house. They had studied together; played on the same city hockey team and then gone on to college together. It was while he was there, going to classes during the day and working as a waiter at night so that he could afford a cubby-hole of an apartment, that his father had come out of a bar one night, slipped on the pavement, fallen into the street and been hit by a car. Jake hadn't shed a tear at his funeral. The money from the sale of the house hadn't amounted to much, the neighbourhood wasn't a good one and the building was in bad shape, but he had salted it away in some good investments that Franklin had suggested to him. Later, he had used the profits as the float for his share in the partnership he and Guy had set up after they graduated.

Life had been good to him after that, Jake thought to himself. The gas and oil exploration business had been lucrative, and he had eventually traded his run-down apartment for a bigger and more glamorous address. He had learned how to hob-nob with politicians and Calgary's moneyed set, and he had more women than he knew what to do with. It had been a surprise to him to discover that women liked him, hell, fell for him in droves, but their adoration was just the icing on the cake. His friendship with Guy stood at the centre of his emotional universe. Not even Guy's marriages, an unhappy first one and the second to Rebecca, had ever seriously interfered with Jake's feelings about him. They were as close as brothers; they understood one another. It was the sort of companionship that was rare between men; Jake knew this and treasured it as a gift beyond value. Although he had never articulated the thought to himself, there hadn't been a woman in his life who had warranted the affection, trust and loyalty that he gave to Guy. Women were expendable commodities, and sex was his for the asking. When various girl-friends had tried to analyse him with deep discussion of his mother, Jake had laughed off their notions. He wasn't the introspective type; he didn't give a damn what had made him the way he was. Life was too short and too good to agonise about the past.

'Air Canada flight 312 from New York now arriving at gate 26.'

The nasal drone of the announcer brought Jake

out of his reverie, and he rose up from his seat, anticipation making him move quickly. Despite the number of women in his life, there was always room for another, and he was curious about Rebecca's sister, Tamara. He knew Rebecca was nursing secret hopes that he would fall for Tamara, marry her and settle down. He had never abused Rebecca of the notion that he was eligible; he just gently ignored her hints and her matchmaking. She had introduced him to a number of women in the past five years and none were his type. Not that they were unattractive; no, it wasn't that. They were all wholesome, pretty and marriageable and that was the drawback. He shied away from women like that; hell, he could feel the vibes of domesticity they gave off a mile away.

They had all been just like Rebecca; wifely and maternal, and much as he liked Guy's wife, Jake simply wasn't in the market for the same thing. Guy was happily married, it was true, but Jake couldn't envision himself being contented in the same set-up. He couldn't imagine being saddled with a wife and two children; he thought that the responsibilities would stifle him. He would go stir-crazy, he would get restless, he didn't know how to be faithful. No, Jake had decided long ago, he didn't want to make some nice woman utterly miserable.

He had received the impression, however, that Tamara wasn't like Rebecca. Guy and Rebecca had dropped some broad hints about her eccentricities and her personality that had sparked his interest. Of course, he was a bit wary as well. A New York actress might consider herself a cut above the Calgary scene; she might have that hard edge of sophistication that made Jake nervous. On the other hand, she just might be beautiful enough to take his breath away, and it was that reasoning that had made him willing to go to the airport in the first place. Jake liked beautiful women. He liked to look at them, he liked to take their clothes off and he liked to make love to them. Jake was no connoisseur of art, but in his opinion, the sight of a beautiful and nude woman lying in his bed beat anything the masters could put on canvas.

As the travellers from the Air Canada flight began to come through the doorway into the lobby, Jake scanned their faces. The only thing he knew about Tamara was that she had distinctive red hair, but he had some preconceived notions about her. Rebecca was tall and shapely with a sweet smile, and he had an inner vision of Tamara that approximated that of her sister. Except for the hair, of course. Rebecca had told him that Tamara had hair the colour of 'oranges at sunset'.

A woman walked through the entrance gate, and he straightened from his slouch against the wall but then slumped back again. She was tall and voluptuous, but her hair was the colour of russet apples and she was greeted warmly by someone else. Her image, however, did imprint itself on Jake's memory as exactly what he thought a New York actress might look like. She would have classically good features, hair that fell in perfect waves and a way of carrying herself that hinted at royalty. The clothes she was dressed in would be understated but decidedly elegant and, if she wore furs, she would have one slung carelessly over her arm, the brown of the ranch mink deep and rich and luxurious.

Jake took a deep breath and smiled to himself. He shifted a bit as he leaned against a wall and jammed his hands into the pockets of his jeans. The thought of the woman he was about to meet made him feel slightly heady and slightly lustful. Although he believed that Tamara would look like Rebecca, he suspected that their sense of morality would be somewhat different. A New York actress, Jake believed, would be sophisticated, knowledgeable and something less than prudish. And he had so much confidence in his own ability to attract women that Jake had some splendid visions dancing through his head and none of them were as innocent as sugar plums. He had already offered to take Tamara around the city, show her the sights and introduce her to Calgary. Rebecca had been delighted.

'Jake!' she had exclaimed. 'Do you really mean it?'

'For you—anything,' he had said magnanimously.

Rebecca had turned to Guy. 'Isn't that wonderful? Isn't it nice of Jake to make the time for Tamara?'

One of Guy's eyebrows had lifted as he glanced at Jake, but Rebecca's enthusiasm had been so sincere and so innocent that he hadn't wanted to disillusion her. 'He's all heart,' he had said, and only Jake had heard the slight edge of sarcasm in his words.

Jake shifted once again as more travellers came through the doorway to be greeted by friends and relatives and he didn't spot one that looked like Tamara Clark. He pushed his stetson to the back of his head, and a frown wrinkled his broad forehead. Damn, he thought. Was she on this flight or what? He pulled a piece of paper out of his pocket, glanced at it and, crumpling it into a little ball, threw it in the nearest litter-bin. It was the right day, the right flight and he was at the right gate. So where the hell was she?

His patience had almost reached the end of its tether when the last passenger finally emerged into the lobby, minutes later than anybody else. The orange hair was like a beacon, its carrot colour glittering in the fluorescent light. Jake had never seen anything like it; he had never seen anything like Tamara before. He wasn't the only person in the waiting-room to glance in her direction and stare, but the others all looked politely away. He was the only one who couldn't stop gaping, his mouth hanging open in pure and utter astonishment.

CHAPTER THREE

TAMARA glanced around the lobby, noticed the
oaf in one corner who was looking stupified by
her appearance, and wondered where Rebecca
was. Although her stomach wasn't sick any
more, she was still terribly tired and the flight had
been nerve-racking. She hadn't known that she
didn't like to fly until she had been strapped into
the seat with the No Smoking sign lit up over her
head. It was then that she had discovered a
strong conviction that nothing with metal wings
and two men in a tiny cockpit would stay up in
the air. Well, she had survived it all and now she
only wanted a strong drink and a bed to crawl in.
Tamara tugged the black Persian lamb coat
around her and tilted the pink fedora she was
wearing at a deeper angle on her head. She had
found the hat in the same shop with the coat and
had fallen for its 'forties glamour and tiny, delicate veil with the miniature pink velvet hearts. Of
course, she had ended up buying it and the coat
and new shoes, spending Mr Freiberg's generous
loan, repaying him when Rebecca wired money
for travel and then, as punishment for her spend-
thrift ways, been forced to go on an all-fluid diet
for two days, the result being that she was now as
thin as . . .

God, but that oaf was still staring at her!

Tamara straightened up, glared at him and looked around once again. She supposed that Calgarians weren't used to a sight that wouldn't even turn a New Yorker's head. Oh, she knew that the Persian lamb was a bit tatty, but she loved its belted line and the way the wide collar made her hair spread out on her shoulders in a huge, carroty fan. She didn't care that the pink of the hat clashed with the red of her hair—it was the kind of non-cliché'd look that she went for. People didn't expect it. Like that bumbling idiot over there—didn't he know his mouth was hanging open? And the shoes, they had been a steal. Teeteringly high heels, as black and shiny as a pair of Mary Jane's with—and this was the best part—tiny pink hearts on the toes.

Where the hell was Rebecca? Tamara would have glanced at her watch but it had broken the week before, and she hadn't had the money to replace it. She knew the plane was late, and it suddenly occurred to her that perhaps Rebecca's baby-sitting arrangements had gone awry and she had been forced to go home. Despite the fact that Tamara was accustomed to manoeuvring around one of the world's most complicated cities, she wasn't used to travelling and anxiety welled within her. She supposed Calgary had cabs and she did have Rebecca's address, but she didn't know how far away it was from the airport and she hardly had any money and . . .

Tamara stared around her, didn't see a clock or a phone booth and, muttering to herself, decided to approach the idiot who was still staring at her

as if she had just been let loose from a zoo. He
wasn't Tamara's type and she barely noticed
what he looked like. She liked men who were
dark, sensuous and dramatic-looking, and this
one hardly filled the bill. He was blond, rugged
and good-looking in an outdoorsy sort of way,
and he was actually wearing one of those hats.
Tamara stared right back at him and wondered if
he roped cows and yodelled as well. Then she
gave a sigh and began to walk towards him. She
would have preferred to approach someone other
than a man who was so obviously shaken by her
appearance that he couldn't stop gaping at her
but, by now, they were the only two people in the
waiting-room.

Tamara stopped before him and said in a loud
voice, 'Could you tell me the time?'

The man's mouth shut with an audible snap
and he cleared his throat. 'I beg your pardon?'

Was he retarded? 'The time,' she said, jabbing
her own wrist to demonstrate what she meant.
'Hours and minutes, big hands, little hands,
seconds.'

He stared down at her, a frown creasing the
bridge of his nose. His eyes were dark brown,
and the skin around them was wrinkled as if he
looked into the sun a lot. He cleared his throat.
'The time,' he said slowly.

'Look, mister, I'm not in the mood for jokes.
Just give me the time.' One heart-spotted toe
tapped impatiently on the carpet.

He slowly pushed the stetson even further
back on his head and glanced up at the ceiling for

a minute. Tamara couldn't believe it. Had this guy just come off the farm? Finally, he said. 'About three.'

'And would you know where the phones are?'

He still seemed mesmerised by her; slowly, one of his thumbs angled over his shoulder. 'That-away.'

Tamara hitched her purse over her shoulder, gave him a withering glance and began to walk away. 'Thank you,' she said sarcastically.

'You don't look like her, you know,' he said from behind her.

Tamara whirled around so quickly that the small veil of her hat billowed out and the tiny hearts floated around her angular face. 'What?'

'I would never have recognised you if it weren't for the hair.'

Tamara was no dope; she knew an attempt at a pick-up when she saw one. The fact that this . . . this cowboy was so inept at making one made her even more furious than she might have been if she weren't so tired and so upset by Rebecca's non-appearance. But she was exhausted and worried and, instead of just walking away and ignoring him, Tamara snapped, 'I'm not interested.'

He was now standing beside her, towering over her actually. Tamara was slightly more than five feet tall in heels; he must have been close to six feet. 'Interested?' he asked in an echo. He still seemed shocked by her appearance; his eyes kept roaming from her face to her hair, down the front of her lamb coat to the tips of her black patent shoes.

'By a drink,' she said, enunciating her words as clearly as she could, 'that is accompanied by meaningless conversation or by a light flirtation that is followed by even more meaningless love-making. I'm not interested in a one-night stand. Got it?'

'A one-night . . .'

'Stand,' she finished for him. 'I'm sure you've heard of one-night stands even in a one-horse town like this. So let's not beat around the bush, whoever you are. I want you to leave me alone.'

He got angry then and the look that came over him made Tamara step back slightly in shock. She wouldn't have thought it was possible for this large, oafish and seemingly less than intelligent male to suddenly appear dangerous, but she hadn't noticed quite how broad his shoulders were in their covering of brown suede until they were being hunched so formidably over her or how big his hands were until they were clenched at his side, the backs of them golden with hair.

Tamara shifted uncomfortably. 'Sorry, I didn't mean to insult your city.'

'What about insulting me?'

Why did men take things so personally and what the hell was she doing still talking to this stranger? 'Forget it,' she shrugged, 'and I have to . . .'

'What makes you think,' he said, 'that I would want to go to bed with a scrawny woman who wears ridiculous clothes, has hair the colour of grated carrots and a personality that would make a lemon pucker?'

It took a lot to render Tamara speechless, but now it was her turn to gape.

'You're not my type, Tamara Clark. You're not my type at all! When I decide to go to sleep with a woman it's because she's feminine and sweet and soft and pleasing.'

Tamara blinked at him and then slowly pulled off her hat so that she could see him better without the veil and delicate hearts. Her hair sprang outwards now that it was released from confinement, and not even the two tortoise-shell barrettes that attempted to hold back her hair were able to restrain the rebellious, tight curls from massing around her face. Without the nose-length veil, he could now see the freckles against the pallor of her skin, orange eyebrows that had been darkened by a pencil and lashes that would have matched her hair if it weren't for their coating of mascara. Jake didn't think he had ever seen anything quite so unappetising as Tamara Clark.

'How the hell do you know my name?'

'I'm here to pick you up.'

'But my sister was . . .'

'Guy's out of town, and Jennifer was so sick that Rebecca had to take her to the hospital.'

Tamara's mouth formed an o and then straightened to form a narrow line. 'How is the baby?'

'She's colicky. I don't think it's anything more than that.'

Tamara nodded as if she were slowly assimilating the information, processing it and then filing it for future storage. When that was done, she gave Jake the full benefit of her attention. 'And who are you?'

'Jake DeBlais.'

He gave her an ironic little bow and swept off his stetson, revealing thick blond hair that was ridged over his ears from the pressure of his hat. He was, Tamara supposed, better-looking than she had first thought although he still wasn't really her idea of handsome. He was very blond, from his hair to the angled golden eyebrows and thick lashes the colour of wheat. His dark eyes were deep-set and he had broad cheekbones that framed a wide mouth and a nose that looked as if it had been in one fight too many. When he grinned at her as he was doing now, she could see the straight line of his teeth.

Her shock was dissipating now, and an innate cockiness was starting to reassert itself. Tamara slowly took a step backwards and very deliberately gave Jake a thorough once-over. She studied the way the opened front of his jacket displayed the muscular contour of his throat; she examined the expanse of his chest beneath the plaid fabric of his shirt.

'So you're the famous Jake,' she finally said.

It was his turn to be disconcerted. 'Famous?'

'Rebecca's told me all about you.'

'Has she?' Jake asked warily.

'Even your vital statistics.' Tamara let her glance drop lower. He was a big man with a broad chest and flat stomach; his jeans were slung low, the circumference of the waist cinched in by a wide black belt with a bronze buckle that had the figure of a bucking bronco etched on it. Her glance lowered some more until it finally came to rest on the zipper of his jeans where the metal curved over the bulge of his flesh. Then she raised her eyes—oh, so innocently—towards his.

It would appear that Jake wasn't fond of having his 'assets' so glibly scrutinised. He looked, for a moment, as if he would take great pleasure in slapping her. 'I don't know what Rebecca told you,' he began.

'That you're sweet and nice and looking for a wife,' she said and just by her tone of voice, Tamara let him know how ridiculous she thought *that* statement was.

Jake winced and then cleared his throat. 'Look, Tamara, let's get this straight. Rebecca has this little fantasy about you and me—that we'll fall in love with one another.'

As an actress, Tamara knew how to laugh, and she put everything she had behind the one she let loose now. The laugh was rich with hilarity as if nothing in this world struck her funny-bone harder than the idea that she and Jake DeBlais could fall in love. When she was done, she gave him a big grin and said, 'That's the most ridiculous thing I ever heard of.'

'I'm glad to see we're thinking along the same lines.'

'I don't believe in marriage,' she continued.

'Good,' he replied. 'Neither do I.'

'Or children or mortgages, weddings or anniversaries.'

'Right.'

'And, frankly, Jake DeBlais, you're not my type either.'

She was standing, facing him, with her purse slung over her shoulder and her head thrown back in defiance; he had put his hands on his hips, his arms akimbo, his legs spread apart, the thick muscularity of them emphasised by the tight fit of his jeans. The venom between them sizzled and crackled in the air. Underneath the smiles and laughter and the presumed meeting of minds over Rebecca's matchmaking, their dislike of one another was as active as a simmering volcano. Jake stared down at her and thought of what she would be like in bed; angular and hard and abrasive. Tamara gazed up at him and thought that she had never seen a man who had so little style. He was as hokey as they came. Brown cowboy boots, faded jeans, a plaid shirt, a suede jacket and a stetson. Straight off the range. And his hands were rough and calloused, and the skin on his face looked as if he stood in the wind for a long time. Oh, she knew he wasn't a cowboy at all, and that he and Guy ran a very successful business, but she could guess what he was like. He would be a jock and a beer drinker. He wouldn't know the first thing about art, ballet, theatre or music. His idea of a good meal would be steak and baked beans. He would like his women dressed in frothy dresses with low-cut bodices and tight waistlines, and his concept of sexy would be a *Playboy* bunny who had a seductive pout and breasts as big as cantaloupes.

'Well,' Jake said through teeth that he had unconsciously clenched together, 'now that you've got that off your chest.' And he gave the buttoned front of Tamara's coat a dismissive glance as if what resided beneath the curly lamb wasn't worth a second thought.

Tamara's chin rose to an even haughtier elevation, and her pale blue eyes narrowed. 'Just so long as we know where we stand.'

'Don't worry, I've got the picture.'

'But for Rebecca's sake, the least we could do is be polite.'

'Of course.'

'I wouldn't want her to be upset.'

'Neither would I.'

There was a short silence and then Tamara said, clearing her throat a bit before she spoke, 'I could take a cab.'

Jake shrugged. 'It's okay. I might as well drive you.'

Tamara would have gladly paid for a cab rather than spend the next half an hour enclosed in a small space with Jake DeBlais, trying to make small-talk and be pleasant to a man she had disliked on the spot. If she had been her old self, she would have insisted and damn the money, but she wasn't her old self. The tendrils of exhaustion were on the move again; the adrenalin that had kept her repartee with Jake alive had dissipated now, and she could feel the tiredness enter her legs and arms. She had a crick at the back of her neck from staring up at him, and she had an overwhelming and undignified urge to yawn in his face. She blamed it on the flight, on the tension of travelling, and on meeting a man whose personality set her teeth on edge. Tamara had no more fight left in her and, unconsciously, she slumped slightly, the strap of her purse slipping down her arm. The only vital part left of her was her hair, and, as she dipped her head to pick up her bag, it glinted in the overhead lights like a thousand copper wires shimmering with electricity.

'All right,' she agreed, straightening up slowly. 'Let's go.'

There had been a sufficient amount of chaos and trauma at the McLaren household that day so that Rebecca's anxiety camouflaged the active antipathy that existed between Jake and Tamara after their drive from the airport. It had been one of those highly uncomfortable times when two people who are totally disinterested in one another and have nothing to say are stuck together in an intimate space. Jake spent it concentrating on the traffic while Tamara sat in the seat beside him, her back perfectly straight, her neck rigid, her eyes on the road. Every once in a while she had slanted her vision slightly to take in the sight of Jake's large hands on the wheel, but then she had looked away and acted as if she were studying the landscape. She must have been successful because Jake only spoke three words to her at the beginning of the trip and three words at the end. When she had climbed into the jeep, he had said, 'Are you okay?' and when they arrived at their destination, he had said, 'This is it.' So much for scintillating and witty conversation.

The McLarens lived on the edge of a suburb in western Calgary, an area of rolling hills that had a magnificent view of the far-off Rockies, which filled the horizon like a chorus of silent grey giants, their white-capped peaks jutting into the blue of the sky. In contrast, the house which was nestled into a hillside appeared small and cozy despite its three levels. It was made of brick and built along a centre door plan, its rooms wide and spacious, the decor picking up the colours of the sky, the mountains and the rolling golden prairie grass that waved along the fields to its right.

As Jake braked in the driveway, the front door opened and Rebecca flew out, her long, dark-red hair streaming up and behind her as the ever-present Calgary wind tossed it into the air. She was much taller than Tamara and built along bigger lines. People rarely thought they were sisters; only the more observant noticed the similarity in eye shape and colour or that the flame of Tamara's hair had been darkened to a deep glow in Rebecca's. As Tamara stepped out of the jeep, Rebecca threw her arms around her, said, 'Oh, Tam, it's so good to see you!' and then promptly burst into tears.

Tamara forgot all about the stress of travelling, her anger at Jake and her own exhaustion. 'Becks, what's the matter?'

Rebecca let go of her and tried to smile. 'I'm sorry, Tam, but it's been such an awful day. And I'm so glad you're here.'

'How's the baby?'

'She's fine. They think she's allergic to regular formula, and that's why she's been so wretched.' She sniffed and then smiled. 'Enough of the miserable McLarens. How about you? Was your trip all right? Did Jake have any problem finding you?'

'The trip was fine, and Jake found me perfectly.'

Rebecca then pushed Tamara away at arm's length and stared at her. 'Where in God's name did you find that coat? No, don't tell me. I can guess.' Rebecca had, before her marriage, lived for a short while with Tamara. She knew all about her sister's strange clothes habits. 'And those shoes!'

Tamara lifted up her hand, the one that was holding her hat, and its veil blew sideways in the wind, the tiny hearts dancing like crazy. 'It matches this.'

'Give me a break,' Rebecca groaned. 'I can't believe they let you across the border. What a monstrosity! You must have shocked poor Jake out of his mind.'

'Well, he . . .'

Jake had just come back after depositing Tamara's bags in the front door of the house. He had jammed his stetson down on his head, and its brim now shaded his face. 'It took some getting used to,' he commented.

Rebecca beamed at both of them. 'I'm so glad you two got a chance to meet.' It was obvious that Rebecca hadn't caught their vibes of dislike. Not that there were any overt indications for her to pick up; Tamara was smiling gaily, and Jake was the perfect gentleman. 'It was so nice of you to get her for us.'

Jake shook his head. 'No problem. It was a pleasure.' He didn't even glance at Tamara when he said it, and she had to give him a few points for his expertise at duplicity. Only she, apparently, had caught the underlying sarcasm in that last word.

'Want to come in for some coffee?'

His response was quick. 'No thanks. I've got some work to do at the office. Besides, I'm sure you and Tamara have a lot to talk about.'

'But I wanted you two to . . .'

Jake bent down and gave Rebecca a kiss on the cheek. 'There's plenty of time for that.'

He was gone then, the wheels of his jeep grinding against the gravel. It was just the sort of car that Tamara had guessed he would drive; it had front-wheel drive, big seats, lots of leg room. He had maps stuck into the visors overhead, a shovel in the back seat and sunglasses hanging over the curve of metal that supported the rear-view mirror. Otherwise the jeep was as clean as a whistle, the chrome polished, the leather gleaming like new. It was the kind of vehicle that was advertised on television as being tough enough to bounce along rocky, mountainous roads and down deep canyons. A tough car for a tough man—the kind who liked steak and baked beans.

Rebecca put her arm through Tamara's as they began to walk towards the house. 'Did you like Jake? What did you think of . . . ?'

Tamara deftly changed the subject. 'Becks, you're looking wonderful.'

'Me?' Rebecca glanced down incredulously at her green cords which were spotted with paint and the man's shirt she wore that was slightly too large for her and stained from having a baby burped on it. 'You must be kidding.'

'Really, marriage and having babies suits you.' It did, too, Tamara thought with a tinge of unexpected envy. Rebecca looked positively blooming. She had once been obese and unhappy with herself, but the weight she had lost before her marriage to Guy had never come back. She would never be willowy or svelte—she was tall and big-boned—but her figure was feminine and curvaceous even in the sloppiest clothes and her face glowed with good health.

Rebecca sighed. 'It does, you know. Even when the kids are being rotten, the house is dirty and I've been up half the night with Jennifer.'

'Is she really going to be all right?'

Rebecca pushed open the front door. 'The doctor says she will be just as soon as we switch her to goat's milk, so I'll have to . . . Tam, you're not interested in this sort of stuff. Now, tell me all about Jake and what you . . .'

'Can I see her?'

'Jennifer? Now?'

Tamara nodded. 'We've never met, you know.'

'Wouldn't you rather change and have a rest before Kevin gets home? We have an hour or so before the carpool brings him back from school.'

Tamara shook her head firmly. 'I'd really like to see Jennifer.'

Rebecca's attention was diverted from Jake and she couldn't help looking as pleased as punch at Tamara's interest in her newest offspring. 'Well, if you really want to. She's sleeping though.'

'I don't mind.'

Tamara had never given much thought to babies. There were none in her world of aspiring actresses, would-be singers and budding writers. Everyone she knew was either single or living with someone in a situation that precluded children. She didn't have any particular aversion to infants; for all she knew, she might even like them. It was simply that, from Tamara's life-style and perspective, babies had always seemed fine for other people and she had preferred to watch them from a distance, if at all. Now, she wasn't really sure what to do when Rebecca opened the door to the nursery, and she approached the white crib gingerly, tip-toeing across the pale yellow carpet.

'Oh, you don't have to be so quiet,' Rebecca said. 'When this kid sleeps, nothing could wake her up.'

Jennifer was tiny and pink with a small snub nose and a wisp of blonde hair capping the round curve of her head. Her eyes were shut tight and her lashes, long and blonde, brushed against her plump cheeks. She slept on her stomach with her nappied rear end in the air and her hands clenched into miniature fists. She was wearing a little shirt that had small pink elephants marching across it in narrow rows, and white booties with pom-pommed ties that gripped at the ankles. The nursery, decorated in yellows and apple green, smelled of baby powder and lotion.

'I can't believe this innocent child kept you up all night,' Tamara said, leaning over the crib and touching her finger very lightly to the fat crease at the back of Jennifer's knee. The baby's skin was softer and smoother than anything Tamara had ever felt before, and she wondered at its texture. 'Mmmm, she's so sweet.'

'Angelic-looking, isn't she?'

'Very.'

Rebecca tucked a loose strand of hair behind her ear and sighed. 'Well, take it from me, Aunt Tamara, she can be hell on wheels. Now, enough of this child adoration. Let me show you your room.'

The guest room was just as Rebecca had promised it would be; soothing, serene and separate from the rest of the family. It was down its own hallway and had an adjoining bath whose tiles matched the Dresden blue of the carpet and the textured wall-paper. White curtains covered a window that overlooked a stretch of prairie and a meandering river in the distance. The bed, a handsome four-poster, had a hand-stitched quilt on it—an old-fashioned design of girls against a background of white. Each girl's parasol, bonnet and high-necked, long-skirted dress was made of a different pattern of calico.

Tamara ran her hand over it and asked, 'Becks, did you make this?'

Rebecca sat down in the rocker in one corner and smiled. 'In one of my spare moments.'

'I didn't know you were into this sort of thing.'

'Marriage has brought out all sorts of new qualities in me.'

Tamara shook her head in amazement. 'The joys of the domestic life.'

'They exist, you know.'

'Not for me,' Tamara denied as she pulled off her coat.

'Still the same old Tamara?'

'Footloose, fancy-free and unattached.'

'No man in your life?'

'Not for a month or so.' Tamara slid her high heels off, wiggled her feet in the carpet and sighed. 'The last one was looking for a meal-ticket. I sent him packing. And the one before that—well, he was boring with a captial B. God, I don't know how I manage to find all the losers.'

'What *did* you think of Jake?'

Tamara had known that she wouldn't be able to keep Rebecca off the subject for ever, and she now shook a reproving finger in her sister's direction. 'How did you arrange it so that sweet baby would cry all morning and you'd have to take her to the hospital?'

Rebecca gave her a rueful smile. 'I'm a match-maker,' she admitted, 'but I wouldn't go to *those* lengths.'

'I'm really not interested in men right now.'

'But what did you think of him?'

Tamara sighed and began to unzip her dress. It was a black shirtwaister with a white collar and cuffs—one of her more conservative outfits. 'He's nice, but . . .'

'But?'

'Believe me, he's not what I'm looking for.'

Rebecca leaned back in the rocker and tucked her foot in the front rung. 'How can you tell? You only saw him for an hour at the most.'

Tamara gave a slightly embarrassed shrug. 'We didn't hit it off.'

'You've had a fight with him already!'

The dress slid to the ground, leaving Tamara in a wispy bra and pantihose. She unlocked her suitcase and rummaged through it. 'I'm a city slicker and he's a hick from the sticks, that's what it amounts to.'

There was a long silence then as Tamara dug out a turtleneck top and a pair of trousers. She hadn't thought Rebecca would like hearing her diagnosis of Jake, but she didn't realise her sister would take it personally. Tamara turned around in order to soften her statement, but Rebecca spoke first.

'What's happened to you?' she asked in a stunned voice.

'I'm just cynical,' she said. 'I can't help it.'

'I'm not talking about that. I'm talking about you. Have you been dieting? Tam, I've never seen you so thin.'

Tamara unconsciously held the turtleneck up

against her chest in an attitude of self-defence.
She knew that she didn't look good; Jake's crack
about her being scrawny had stung hard. She was
bonier and more angular than she had ever been.
Her shoulder-blades stuck out like knobs; her
spine was a bumpy ridge. Her stomach had gone
from flat to concave in the last month, and her
hip-bones jutted out like blades against her skin.

'Not dieting exactly,' she began.

'Have you been eating properly?'

'Rebecca, just because you were trained as a
nurse doesn't mean that . . .'

But her sister had stood up now, marched over
to her and was turning Tamara around so that she
faced the merciless sun whose rays were angling
in through the window. She blinked in the brightness and Rebecca said in a grim tone, 'I wondered
about all that make-up.'

'I'm a bit run-down.'

'A bit run-down! That must be the understate-
ment of the year. You look terrible.'

Tamara tried to make light of it. 'Com-
plimentary, aren't you?'

'Tam, what's going on? You look undernourished; you've got circles under your eyes a
mile deep.'

Tamara's shoulders slumped. 'I'm tired,' she
confessed. 'And money's been so tight that sometimes I skip meals.'

'And you're still trying to take three lessons a
day and hold down two jobs, right?'

'It's . . . been hectic.'

'Have you gone to see a doctor?'

'I don't need a doctor. Just some sleep and three meals a day.'

Rebecca put her arms around Tamara and hugged her hard. 'You can sleep all you want here, and you're way too skinny. I'm going to fatten you up, if I have to force the food down your throat. Got it?'

Tamara nodded obediently. It was wonderful to have Rebecca taking charge, ordering her around and running her existence. That was one of the reasons she had come. She had no longer been able to bear the responsibility of herself; the burdens had become too much for her to carry on her own. And Rebecca was superb at taking care of people. It wasn't that she was bossy or manipulative; that had been Martine's role. Rebecca was a born nurturer. Look at the peaceful rooms of the house and the baby sleeping so sweetly in its crib. Her calming touch was everywhere, and it spread like a balm over Tamara's agitated and tired soul.

'. . . protein and vegetables,' Rebecca was saying, 'and maybe an iron supplement. We'll start with that.'

Tamara nodded and smiled and closed her eyes against the white glare of the sun. It had been years since she had let anyone tell her what to do, but her independence was slipping away from her like sand sifting through open fingers. It felt so wonderful that Tamara didn't see it as the first crack in the armour of her presumed invincibility; she didn't think of it as a yielding or a giving in. She was so accustomed to being in complete and total control of herself that she envisioned her stay with Rebecca as merely a vacation from responsibilities.

It didn't occur to Tamara that a part of herself that had been crushed during her years of fierce independence was now coming to the surface and clamouring for attention. A softer Tamara was emerging, the one that her parents' divorce and the actions of Martine had forced into hiding. Tamara didn't know it but, just as her body was starved of sleep and food, her psyche was starved of mothering. She had never had enough of it; she didn't even recognise what it was when it came her way. She only knew that she loved the feeling of it.

'Okay,' she said.

'And an afternoon nap. You and Jennifer can hit the hay together. In fact, you can start now.'

Tamara glanced at the bed; it was big and inviting. 'Now?'

'Now,' stated Rebecca firmly. 'And if you don't get in there fast, I'll tuck you in myself.'

But Rebecca's regime for Tamara didn't work as well as either of them thought it would, although first impressions were that everything was going fine. The days were peaceful; with Guy on business up in the Arctic and Kevin going full-time to kindergarten, there were only the gentle rhythms of eating and sleeping and baby-watching. Tamara slept for hours, not only at night, but also for long naps during the day. And she was eating prodigiously. She had eggs, bacon and toast in the morning, a three-course meal at lunch and a delicious, gourmet concoction that Rebecca would put together for dinner. With each meal, she took vitamins and iron tablets and obediently drank the glass of milk that Rebecca set before her. Tamara hadn't touched milk in ten years at least, but Rebecca had vetoed coffee except for one cup at breakfast.

It was an autocratic regime, but Tamara submitted to it with barely a grumble. She was too tired to argue or fight back. It was as if her body, long deprived and undernourished, had taken over her mind. Even when she had napped only two hours before and she thought she should be able to stay awake, her eyes would start closing and she would be forced to lie down and sleep some more. And, when she had crawled into bed and succumbed to this unending exhaustion, her sleep was heavy and deep and black. She never dreamed any more; she simply seemed to slip into a dark oblivion.

And she ate as if her body were a hollow crying out to be filled. She craved carbohydrates with almost an obsessive need. For years she had dieted to the point that she had verged on emaciation; it had almost become a way of life. Now, she threw all caution to the winds and indulged in breads and rolls and croissants; she couldn't seem to get enough of them. Every once in a rare while, Tamara worried about her figure, but the future seemed so far away to her that it was easy to put the worry aside. Without classes to go to and auditions to agonise over and the constant stress of wondering if she would get a part, Tamara had given up thinking of anything beyond the next minute. She simply didn't have the energy to care.

Rebecca watched her, made sure that she was eating a balanced diet and saw, to her satisfaction, that Tamara had lost the circles under her eyes, the gauntness in her face and that look of being a pale ghost with a halo of fire around her head. She had just started congratulating herself on bringing her sister out of this crisis of neglect when she found Tamara coming out of the bathroom one afternoon, visibly shaking beneath the blue quilting of her robe.

'What's the matter?' she asked in alarm.

Tamara leaned against the wall and put a trembling hand to her forehead. She had been sweating and her skin gleamed an unhealthy shade of white. 'I just threw up.'

Rebecca stared at her. 'I wonder if you've caught flu.'

Tamara's eyes were wide and frightened. 'I threw up a couple of times in New York, too.'

'Let's give it a day or two,' Rebecca comforted her. 'It may just be a passing bug.'

But it wasn't; the nausea and the sporadic vomiting persisted. Rebecca, who had professionally assessed Tamara as overworked and under stress, began to worry in earnest. Mentally, she went through the litany of illnesses that Tamara could have and none of them was reassuring. She had already thought of anaemia or mononucleosis, but more serious blood diseases came to mind and she finally decided that Tamara had to go to a doctor. She overcame all of Tamara's concerns about money, saying that she and Guy had more than enough to afford her medical care, and refused to listen to Tamara's ridiculous assertions that there was nothing basically wrong with her. It was quite evident to Rebecca that her sister was petrified of doctors and terrified to find out the truth.

She called her family doctor, made an appointment, got a baby-sitter for Jennifer and drove Tamara to the clinic.

'Now, make sure and tell him everything,' Rebecca encouraged as they sat down in the waiting-room.

Tamara glanced around her and grimaced. 'I hate the way the medical profession insists on being so goddamn cheerful. Colourful pictures, plants and cartoons pinned up on the walls.'

'Don't forget to mention how sick you were before you came here.'

Tamara picked up a batch of brochures on the table beside her and stared at them. '"Nutrition is Good for You,"' she read aloud in a dramatic voice. '"A New Mother's Guide to Breastfeeding." "Arthritis and You." Oh, God.'

Rebecca ignored her. 'Tam, tell him that you haven't been to a doctor in years and make sure that he takes some blood tests.'

Tamara hunched down in her chair and looked small and miserable. 'I hate doctors.'

'This one is very nice. You'll like him.'

'I doubt it.'

The nurse, efficient and crisp in white, stepped into the room. 'Tamara Clark? This way, please.'

Rebecca smiled as Tamara followed the nurse. It was amazing the way Tamara could communicate her feelings without even talking. Her walk as she headed into the office displayed reluctance and hostility mixed with resignation. It had something to do with the way she held her head and the squaring of her shoulders. Rebecca pulled a magazine off the rack next to her and flipped open the first page, but she didn't really read what was there. She was thinking that she had never really understood what made Tamara tick. Her sister had always been the dramatic one in the family, the daughter with the strongest and most vivid personality. Everything she said or did was a theatrical pose. She struck attitudes; she exaggerated her emotions. Even her bizarre clothes were a means to an end; a way, Rebecca had often thought, of deceiving the eye of the beholder.

You couldn't really tell what Tamara was thinking or predict what she would do next. Rebecca wasn't fooled by her docility of the past week. It was only a phase that would end when her energy returned. Then the old Tamara would come back; intense, hard-edged and driven. Rebecca blamed it on Martine, of course. She had never known what had caused the rift between her mother and Tamara, but the chasm had been so wide and so fraught with anger and malice that neither of them had been able to bridge it. When

she was seventeen, young and very naïve,
Tamara had left home, never to return. Rebecca
could still remember watching her sister pack,
throwing her clothes into a large duffel bag with
a ferocious anger, a litany of hatred pouring
out of her in a vitriolic stream. 'I feel sorry for
you,' she had said to Rebecca, 'having to stay
here with that bitch. I hate her. God, how I hate
her.'

Rebecca had begged Tamara to stay; she had
been the one who was crying, but nothing she
had said worked. Tamara had left that night on
the bus to New York with one hundred dollars in
her pocket. Martine had only said grimly, 'It's her
bed, now she can lie in it.' Rebecca had grieved
for weeks.

Oh, she knew why Tamara had come to
Calgary after . years of countless and often
unanswered invitations. Although her sister
hadn't discussed her career at all, Rebecca sensed
that Tamara's failure to make it on the Broadway
stage lay behind the illness and the unhappiness
and the sudden flight from New York. Her home
was merely a place where Tamara could catch her
breath and regroup her forces. Rebecca didn't
mind that she was being used in that way;
Tamara had once done it for her—before she had
married Guy. Tamara had taken her into her tiny
apartment, fed her and soothed her spirit; she
was glad to offer her payment in kind.

Of course, she also had hopes that Tamara
would not only regain her health, but that she
also might settle down. Rebecca didn't know why

she had decided that Jake would be the perfect mate for her sister, but she was convinced that this was so. Not that he realised it. Jake claimed he was the world's happiest bachelor, but when Rebecca watched him play with Kevin and hold Jennifer, she had her doubts about his contentment. He loved children, and he loved to come to the McLaren house. He hung around during the weekends; he helped Guy with the yard work; occasionally, he even cooked for them. Rebecca was positive that inside that amiable bachelor façade was a family man screaming to come out. Guy said she was crazy; that no woman in the world would convince Jake to ensnare himself in the tangles of matrimony. And when Rebecca had mentioned Tamara, he had given her a look of pure astonishment. But what did Guy know, Rebecca thought. He didn't have her feminine intuition; he didn't have the sixth sense that pointed directly towards Tamara and . . .

The door to the office opened and Tamara walked out.

'The lab is two floors down,' the nurse was saying in a cheerful voice. 'And when you're done there, you can come back.'

Tamara looked as if she were sleep-walking. There was a somnambulistic quality to the way her eyes looked into the distance and her face was absolutely blank. She was pale, too; paler even than she had been the day she had arrived in Calgary, and Rebecca could see that her hand was trembling. She was carrying a sheaf of prescriptions and requests for lab services, and they fluttered slightly like leaves caught in a chill breeze.

Rebecca stood up, feeling her heart catch in her throat. 'Tam?' she called softly, not caring about the other people in the waiting-room or the way they were staring at her sister. She walked to Tamara's side. 'Tam?'

Tamara finally blinked as if she had come out of a dark place and into the light, but she stood absolutely still, her blue eyes wide with shock. 'Oh, God,' she moaned.

Panic rose in Rebecca. She gripped Tamara's other hand. 'Tam, are you all right? Is it . . . something serious?'

Her sister was slowly coming back to life. She swallowed, grimaced and then cleared her throat. 'It's not fatal, if that's what you mean.'

'What did the doctor say?'

'I'm pregnant, that's what he said. Two months pregnant.'

CHAPTER FOUR

JAKE was having a rough week. With Guy gone, the office work was piling up and recent negotiations on a gas exploration project had come to a halt over the estimated expenses for machinery. It meant that Jake had to lean on his subcontractors to lower their prices and that was always unpleasant. Guy was far better at that sort of thing than he was. It was Jake who could analyse the project on paper and put together a group that would do the work. He supplied the theory and Guy the practical force behind it. They were a good team, and Jake only operated at half his level of efficiency when Guy was out of the office.

Then there was the jeep, the dishwasher and his squash game. The first had developed transmission problems, the second had gone on the blink and the third had caused him acute mortification. He had been the favoured contender in his club's squash tournament, and he had been beaten, albeit only by a point, but beaten nonetheless. His opponent had proved to have a backhand of such deadly accuracy that it had been all Jake could do to maintain a solid defence. There had been a party afterwards where beer was drunk by the gallon and the jokes were rampant. Jake and his opponent had sat by one another and had both got appropriately soused so that they seemed like the best of pals, but the following morning when Jake awoke with the painful sensation that a guillotine would be the only remedy to alleviate the throbbing ache in his head, he discovered that he was a sore loser. Next time, he vowed he would beat the pants off that bastard.

Then there was his social life, which seemed to be not only at loose ends, but for all intents and purposes non-existent. It was a rare moment when Jake's little black book couldn't supply him with at least half a dozen names of women who were available and willing, but for some reason the ones he had called were no longer ripe for plucking. Louise was a woman whom he often phoned when an empty evening loomed ahead. She was petite, curvaceous and always ready for some fun. Her answering machine was equally bubbly, breathless and full of words that sounded as if they were marked with italics. Unfortunately, it was also dismissive.

'Hi! This is Louise speaking and I'm *so* sorry that I can't talk to you right now but, if you know how I *feel* about the Calgary winter, I'm sure you'll understand why I *simply* couldn't pass up the chance to visit Acapulco. Just leave your name and number after the beep, and I *promise* I'll call you just as soon as I get back from lounging in the *sun* . . . Beep.'

'Acapulco,' Jake muttered under his breath as he consulted his telephone book. 'Acapulco.'

Samantha shocked him by saying that she had

decided to go back to school and was taking night courses.

'In what?' Jake was trying to imagine the tall, dark-haired and voluptuous Samantha being studious and failed. Her favourite pastime had been lolling under a heating lamp so that her body would have the perfect, uniform tan.

'Business administration.'

'You're joking.'

'No, Jake. I've changed, you see; I've become serious about life.'

And then there was Carla. She was his last hope after ten phone calls had turned up nothing but duds. Carla was sweet, friendly and liked to cuddle. They had never had much in common except the occasional bedroom fling, but when they did get together, it was always enjoyable.

Carla, however, was the last straw.

'Hey, babe. It's Jake.'

'Jake? Jake DeBlais?'

'Right. Long time, no see.'

'It's been a year, hasn't it?'

'Has it? It seems like yesterday.'

'Come on, Jake. I bet you can't even remember the colour of my hair.'

'Sure I can.' Jake checked the scribble he had written in beside Carla's phone number. 'It's light brown with streaks of honey in it.'

Carla laughed. 'You're so cute,' she said. 'Such a poet.'

'Are you free this Saturday? Would you like to take in a movie and dinner?'

'You're too late, sweetheart. I'm booked.'

'How about during the week?'

'I'm booked then, too.' There was a hint of a giggle in her voice.

'Next Saturday?'

'Actually, I got married about three months ago.'

'Married!'

'Tied the knot before a minister and bought a Cuisinart.'

A domesticated Carla was beyond Jake's imaginative capacities. 'And who is the . . . lucky guy?'

'No one you know. A fellow I met in Bible class.'

Jake almost dropped the phone. 'Bible class!'

'It sounds crazy, I know, but one day I looked around me and saw that my life was a mess and took a Bible class. I've got my head together now; I'm really very happy.'

'Well, listen . . . hey, that's great. Congratulations and all that.'

'Thanks, Jake. Bye now.'

'Bye.'

He had hung up the telephone, muttered, 'Holy s—' under his breath and finally decided to ask out the woman in his life who had never, in his experience, let him down.

Cordelia McLaren was dressed up to the nines for her dinner out with Jake. Her diminutive frame was outfitted in an elegant grey wool suit with a mauve silk blouse, and she wore around her neck and on her ears the diamonds that Franklin had given her for their thirtieth wedding anniversary. Her grey hair was brushed back and coiled at her neck into a chignon, and her eyes were artfully made up so that their blue snapped and glittered at him from behind her glasses. Although there were wrinkles on her face and her hands were slightly bent with arthritis, Jake thought she had never looked lovelier and told her so.

Cordelia gave him a shrewd look over the dinner table. They were seated at the corner of what appeared to be a room decorated as an Indian tepee with its roof enclosed in angled canvas and its walls dotted with Indian relics. The restaurant was pursuing a Wild West theme with a vengeance and had its waiters in Indian headdresses and fringed buckskin with their faces made up to look like braves on the war-path. Jake thought the whole set-up was corny, but the chef knew how to cook a hell of a good steak.

'Thank you,' she said dryly and then added, 'and to what do I owe this honour?'

Jake filled both his goblet and hers with a wine the colour of rubies. He was wearing a grey suit, a shirt with a faint blue pin-stripe and a silvery tie. His hair gleamed golden in the dim illumination, and the lamp-light touched on a cheekbone, the thickness of a pale eyebrow and the reflection of a dark eye. The formality of his attire didn't sit as comfortably on him as it did on other men. There was something big, raw and powerful about Jake that made a suit seem merely like a superficial veneer. 'To an old friendship,' he answered easily, 'to the onset of winter, to Guy's return tomorrow. You choose.'

'I think,' she remarked, appraising his grey suit, white shirt with faint blue pin-stripes and the silver and blue tie, 'that you were lonely.'

'Now, why don't women ever think men can be happy on their own?'

'Because, ninety-nine times out of a hundred, they are not.'

Jake gave her an ironic smile and raised his wine glass. 'To the blissful state of bachelorhood.'

'You can't fool me,' replied Cordelia tartly. 'I'm merely a substitute for someone younger and far sexier.'

Jake knew all the ways that Cordelia was capable of angling for information. She was persistent, clever and insightful; he had never been able to keep a secret from her when he was younger, and he knew damn well he wouldn't be able to now, but the game of hide and seek was half the fun. Cordelia was the only woman Jake knew who was able to whet the lazy edge of his intelligence. He was far too amiable to spar with other people; he didn't like arguments, debates or verbal skirmishes. But he enjoyed Cordelia's conversation with great relish. The truth was that they understood one another very well.

'Cordelia,' he said, 'you underrate yourself. You're a very foxy lady for sixty-five.'

'I can smell an evasion a mile away,' she warned him as the waiter put their plates before them.

'Well,' Jake said, 'my dishwasher broke.'

Cordelia gave an unladylike snort. 'So?'

'And the jeep needs its transmission fixed.'

'And?'

'And I lost the squash tournament.'

'I think I'm seeing the light at the end of the tunnel. Keep going.'

'And neither Louise nor Samantha nor Carla were even the slightest bit interested in hearing from me.'

'Ah-ha. And who precisely are Louise, Samantha and Carla?'

'Old friends.'

'Old friends,' she echoed him. 'Tell me, Jake, hasn't a woman come along yet that's worth more than a friendship?'

'Cordelia,' he smiled gallantly, 'if you were thirty years younger, I would be proposing to you right now.'

She couldn't help smiling at him. 'You are such a flirt,' she said. 'It's shameful.'

'But you like it,' he pointed out.

'Of course I do, but I'm only human. Anyway, you're still evading the issue. What's wrong with these women?'

Jake shrugged. 'I haven't met the right one yet.'

Cordelia leaned forward. 'It's your mother, you know. You don't trust women.'

'I love amateur psychology,' Jake grinned. 'Tell me more about my psyche.'

'And pander to your already inflated ego?'

'Inflated ego! Cordelia, I'm crushed.'

'I doubt it,' she said and then glanced at his

plate, 'and eat before your food gets cold.'

Jake laughed at her. 'Whenever you lose an argument, you fall back on to motherhood.'

Cordelia gave him a mock-glare and put a dollop of sour cream on to her baked potato. 'What did you think of Rebecca's sister?' she asked.

Jake grimaced. 'Skinny and nasty.'

'Ouch.' Cordelia winced. 'Isn't that a little strong?'

'I didn't like her.'

'Rebecca had great hopes pinned on a love affair between the two of you.'

'Rebecca has always been something of a romantic dreamer, don't you think?'

'Yes, but she's a sweetheart. I now have a happy son and two lovely grandchildren, thanks to Rebecca. I can forgive her that idealism.'

'At any rate,' Jake continued, 'the feeling was mutual. Tamara didn't like me any more than I liked her.'

'She's ill, you know.'

'Have you seen her?'

Cordelia shook her head. 'She's been too sick for company. Rebecca took her to the doctor today, but I haven't heard anything yet. She's afraid that Tamara might have some sort of blood disease. Anaemia perhaps.'

'Rebecca will nurse her back to health,' Jake said. 'I always hope that if I get sick, I'll have Rebecca at my bedside. She has that touch.'

Cordelia wagged a finger at him. 'It's mothering you need,' she chided. 'That's my diagnosis.

The trouble is that you won't let any woman close enough to you to try.'

They had had this conversation before, and it was one that Jake could parry lightly and with ease, but it always left him feeling distinctly uncomfortable. He was well aware that his relationships with women were shallow, insubstantial and basically not satisfying in any emotional way, but he was loath to change a pattern of behaviour that was painless and physically pleasant. And he had no intention of thinking about his childhood; those were memories that he had buried deep within. He hadn't done this consciously; he hadn't deliberately put aside his past. It had been the only way he had been able to survive the loss of his mother, the abuse of his father and years when he was helpless and unhappy. The memories were far too dangerous and far too upsetting to come to the surface.

'Oh, no, you don't,' Jake said quickly. 'No more pop analysis. We're going to talk about you now.' He tilted his head and appraised her. 'There's something different about you. I don't know exactly what . . . I've got it now, it's your hair.'

'I've darkened it,' she replied calmly. 'It was going too white.'

This time it was Jake who looked shrewd. Although Cordelia liked to be attractive, she wasn't the sort to fuss about her appearance and, as far as he had known, she had allowed herself to age gracefully without resorting to artifice. 'Interesting,' he said.

'No, it isn't. It's vanity.'

'But I've never known you to be vain.'

'There's a lot you don't know about me, Jake DeBlais.'

'Like the fact that you've found yourself a boy-friend?'

Jake knew he had hit the nail on the head the moment he said it. Cordelia tried to stare him down, failed and then, leaning forward, clasped her hands together with suppressed delight. 'I've been dying to tell someone, but I've been afraid to say anything to Guy. You know how he felt about his father, and I'm worried that he'll be upset that another man is taking his father's place. Of course, no one could really take Franklin's place. He was such a wonderful man and a good father and husband and . . .'

'Whoa,' Jake cried, holding up his hand. 'Are you trying to say that you're getting married again?'

Cordelia blinked. 'Heavens no. I'd never want to get married again.'

'But you've met a man.'

When Cordelia smiled, dimples appeared in her cheeks. 'A really lovely person. He's a retired stockbroker. Well, actually, I knew him a bit when Franklin was still alive, but only in passing. His wife died last year; he has three children and six grandchildren. We met at the library, of all places. He was in the biography section, and I was looking for a book on Oriental carpets and we just happened to bump into one another. It was only a month ago.'

Jake shook his head in amazement. 'Cordelia, you take my breath away.'

Cordelia gave him a mock-frown. 'You're laughing at me.'

'Never,' Jake said solemnly. 'I'd never laugh at you, not even if you fell head over heels in love, jumped into bed with the first old-age pensioner you met and lived in sin for the rest of your life.'

Cordelia leaned forward and said in a confidential whisper, 'We have talked about living together, but only a little.'

'Really?'

'Really.'

'And no hint of wedding bells?'

Cordelia dismissed the notion with a shrug. 'Marriage is for people who want to have children and mortgages together. Besides, it would complicate the issue of wills and money and inheritances. It's not necessary.'

Jake eyed her with affection. 'It doesn't sound like you've let love and sex go to your head.'

Cordelia had the grace to blush, but she picked up her wine glass as if to hide it. 'Now, Jake . . .' she began.

'You have gone to bed with him, haven't you?'

She wagged a finger in his direction. 'Just because you have never had a platonic relation . . .'

'Come on, Cordelia. I wasn't born yesterday. 'Fess up.'

'Well,' she said. 'He's not eighteen, you know. He's almost seventy.'

'But . . . ?'

She gave him a small and suddenly shy smile. 'There's life left in the old boy yet.'

Jake lifted his wine glass and touched it to hers. 'A toast. May you have many more rolls in the hay.'

Cordelia put her wine glass down. 'You're outrageous,' she reproved tartly and without much conviction. 'Now, how am I going to tell Guy?'

'Guy's a big boy now. He'll adjust.'

'I want him to like Henry.'

'If you like him, we'll all like him. Don't worry about it.'

Jake had never seen Cordelia look so uncertain. 'You're sure?'

'I'm absolutely positive,' he nodded. 'Now, eat up before your food gets cold. Besides, I'm going to order you some cheesecake for dessert. It's great here; it'll melt in your mouth.'

'It's too fattening.'

'I'll bet Henry likes a woman with some meat on her bones.'

'I . . .'

'Come on, foxy lady,' Jake charmed her with his wide grin. 'I don't want to be the only sinner in the family.'

At the same time that Jake was out to dinner with Cordelia, Rebecca and Tamara were seated in the living room sharing a large pot of coffee and covering ground they had covered half a dozen times that day. The children were asleep, the curtains were closed and one light shed its golden glow over the tans, beiges and golds of the furniture and the carpet. Both women were in nightgowns and bathrobes, and Tamara was curled up on the couch with a blanket around her. Rebecca was knitting a sweater she was making for Guy and the clicking of her needles formed a background motif to their discussions. Tamara periodically pulled the blanket closer to her and sipped away at coffee that was so hot it almost burnt her tongue. She didn't care; she was chilled to the bone. She hadn't been able to stop shivering since leaving the doctor's office that afternoon.

Not that he wasn't as nice as Rebecca had claimed. He had smiled at her, tried to make her feel comfortable and was pleasantly nonjudgmental about his findings. She was rundown, he had told her, possibly anaemic and absolutely pregnant. Her nausea wasn't uncommon for the first three months, but it was important that she concentrate on building up her strength. He hadn't asked her about a husband and had been kind enough not to react to the expressions that must have crossed her face. Tamara had felt herself go very hot at first and then very cold. A chill seemed to have settled deep in her bones, and she couldn't shake it. Her fingertips were like ice, and her nails were slightly blue. Not even the coffee, burning its way down her throat, warmed the frozen centre of her.

The irony of the whole thing was that, if she had thought about it, Tamara would have guessed that she was pregnant. She had noticed the fact that her period hadn't come, but then she was often irregular so it hadn't alarmed her. The swelling of her breasts had also seemed inconsequential to her. In fact, she had merely assumed that it was a precursor to the menstrual cycle that was slow in coming. Of course, the tiredness and nausea should have triggered a suspicion of pregnancy, but Tamara had been so busy and so out of tune with her own body, that she had never made the connection at all. The doctor's announcement had, therefore, come right out of the blue, striking her with all the force of a thunderbolt.

'I can't believe it,' she repeated for the millionth time.

'Tam, it can happen to anyone.'

'If only I hadn't stopped taking birth control pills. At least they're a hundred per cent effective.'

'You couldn't tolerate them any more.'

'And I thought a diaphragm would be just as safe.'

'You're not the only woman who's got pregnant that way.'

They were both silent for a bit. Rebecca picked up the pattern for the sweater she was knitting, studied it for a moment and then bent over her needles again. Tamara watched yarn smoothly running through her sister's fingers and the glint of the quickly moving needles. Life had always seemed so simple to her . . . perhaps, uncomplicated was a better word. She had seen her existence as a formula—it was Tamara pitted against the world. First there had been her mother and then Manhattan and the theatre. She had fought, battled and scratched her way to a lifestyle that accommodated her needs. She usually had food in the kitchen, clothes on her back and the freedom to pursue her career.

Tamara had never let anything come between her and the goal of stardom. From the time she was seventeen, naïve and so broke that she had been forced to bunk down in a cockroach-infested hostel on the lower East side, Tamara had single-mindedly followed the path to a Broadway role. She had got a job as a waitress, haunted the theatres and taken lessons. Slowly, she had built up contacts and learned the craft of acting. Tidbits had been thrown her way; gossip that suggested a small part in an established show might go to an unknown, a lover who had introduced her to the producer of an avant-garde company, one of those unexpected breaks when the star gets sick and her understudy is thrust into the limelight for a brief time. Each minor success had led Tamara to fight harder for the major one that surely loomed on the horizon. And she had let nothing get in her way; not friends, not relatives, not lovers.

'I don't even know who it was,' Tamara confessed.

Rebecca looked up from her knitting. 'The father, you mean?'

'It could have been the parasite or boring with a capital B. They were both hanging around two months ago. And I started an affair with one before finishing with the other.'

'It doesn't really matter, does it? You didn't have any intention of seeing either one of them again anyway.'

'No, but I suppose I have a sort of academic interest. They were both so different. The first one was young, blond and sort of cute in an adolescent way. His ears still stuck out a bit. And the other was older, dark-haired and obsessed with himself. I really didn't like him.'

'Why did you sleep with him then?'

'I didn't know he spent his time navel-gazing,' Tamara said. 'He was a writer with a good sense of humour and a way of sending me flowers. I was momentarily bowled over by this spurt of romanticism on his part and didn't notice that all he talked about was himself.'

'And the first one—why him?'

'An aspiring actor, young and sweet and wor-shipping. He adored me, it was refreshing—for a time.'

'Oh, Tam, when will you ever learn?'

'Learn what?'

'That sleeping around has never made you happy.'

A week ago, Tamara would have bristled at that statement. She would have taken it as a judgment on her lifestyle and personal choices; she would have seen it as derogatory and insult-ing and ultra-conservative. But Rebecca wasn't the type to impose her moral beliefs on someone else and, besides, in her heart Tamara agreed with her. What had started out in her life as the occasional fling for variety, for fun and for companionship had turned into something demeaning and sordid. And casual sex had repercussions far beyond anything Tamara had dreamed possible. Tonight, she carried the result of an indifferent coupling inside her, a seed sown without thought or caring. And in seven months, it was possible that that tiny seed would be like Jennifer; pink, soft, dependent and demanding.

'There was no alternative,' Tamara replied with a slight shrug. 'I never met a man I'd want to stay with.'

'You don't trust men enough.'

Tamara's voice was bitter. 'Should I, after what our father did?'

'Not all men are like that. Some of them care; some of them want families and stability and commitment.'

'Becks, you found a needle in a haystack. Believe me, most of what's out there is cynical, exploitative and greedy. I know—I've been there and back too many times.'

Rebecca sighed, knowing how futile it was to talk to Tamara about men. Her sister had a shield around her so thick and so solid that no man had ever been able to penetrate it to the woman inside. Their father's abandonment of the family had turned Martine into a bitter, vengeful woman and had affected all his daughters differently. Rebecca had eaten herself into obesity, Tamara hated men and Celia was withdrawn. None of them had been unscathed by the vicious animosity that had developed between their parents or the way their father had dropped the burden of them all, leaving one day without a word, discarding them as if they were so much detritus in his life.

'Let's not argue,' she said. 'The real issue is the abortion. It isn't as easy to get one here as it is in New York. But I hate the thought of sending you there to go through it on your own. I'd much rather have you with us.'

Tamara clutched the blanket more tightly around her as if a cold wind had sprung up in the room. 'I don't . . .'

'It's not as bad as you think,' Rebecca reassured her. 'You're only two months pregnant. And it's just an outpatient procedure, it's not a hospitalisation. Still, I know it can be traumatic and I'd like to be with you.'

'I don't know,' Tamara whispered.

Rebecca put down her knitting. 'Know what?'

'Whether I want to or not.'

'I know how much you hate doctors and hospitals, but you mustn't let squeamishness get in the way of . . .' She paused as the impact of what Tamara had said finally dawned on her. 'You mean—you don't want an abortion?'

Tamara sank down even more deeply into the folds of the blanket. 'I don't know,' she whispered miserably.

'Tam, you're not serious, are you?' And then at the expression on her sister's face, Rebecca added, 'You don't have any money or a stable career, you don't care about the father, whoever he is, and you've never wanted a baby in your life.'

'I know.'

'Then why would you want to go through with it?'

It was an impossible question because Tamara herself did not know the answer to it. Of course, her first reaction had been the same as Rebecca's, even more so. She knew just how incompatible her life-style was with an infant's. She didn't have a decent home, a steady income or a husband; she lived from hand-to-mouth, coming in late at night and sleeping in late in the morning. She was admittedly selfish and self-centred; Tamara had spent years thinking of no one else but herself.

But something insidious was working inside of her, and Tamara didn't know precisely what it was. She saw the future stretching out in front of her and part of her said, 'Is that all there is?' She felt an emptiness at the core of her and saw the frenetic pace of her life as a façade, a way of filling up time, a scurry of activity that obscured the reality of being Tamara Clark. Perhaps it was the slowly-growing realisation that she might never be a great actress that had made her sit back and view her life from a totally different perspective; perhaps it was the shock of discovering that, despite all one's plans, life has a way of following its own devious path; perhaps, and this thought hinged on the fact that Tamara, like many actresses, had a host of superstitions about luck and fate, perhaps the pregnancy was an act of destiny, an augur of something new, a sign from the gods pointing in a direction she had never faced.

Tamara wasn't quite capable of articulating any of this; the emotions were jumbled about within her, raw and undefined and turbulent. She only knew that they blurred her thoughts and made her shrink back from making a decision. They made her look at Rebecca with a helpless expression and answer her question with an indecision that was completely alien to her character.

'I don't know,' she said slowly and then shivered some more. 'I really don't know.'

Guy came home the next day while Rebecca and Tamara were in the kitchen with the children. Rebecca was making dinner while Kevin, aged five, was ostensibly helping her mix blueberry muffins but was, in reality, making a mess. There were lumps of muffin mix on the counters and several smears of blueberry across his face. Not that the difficulties of baking had deterred Kevin from his enthusiastic application of the wooden spoon. He was mixing vigorously, his small features fierce with concentration. He was small and dark-haired and looked like a miniature version of his father. Tamara had already discovered that Kevin refused to be kissed, hugged or otherwise treated in an affectionate fashion. He had reached a stage, Rebecca said, where signs of love were considered babyish, a reaction to Jennifer's birth.

The sound of the front door opening and Guy's voice made Rebecca drop her dishcloth, whirl around and run out to the hallway with Kevin right behind her, yelling, 'Daddy! Daddy!'

Tamara looked at Jennifer. 'That leaves us, baby,' she said.

Jennifer was drumming a spoon on the table of her high chair and grinning like a maniac. She was just barely sitting up and had only recently graduated from her infant seat to more grown-up accommodations. Rebecca had propped her up on both sides with rolled-up towels, but she still had a tendency to slide to a slight angle. This odd perspective on the world didn't seem to bother Jennifer at all. She burbled at Tamara and drooled.

'Very becoming,' Tamara teased as she approached Jennifer with a flannel. 'Your father isn't going to want to see you with a wet chin.'

Jennifer didn't like to have her face washed; she twisted and squirmed and her features, tiny and round, screwed up into a grimace. Tamara gingerly applied the washcloth to her face, following the small head around as it moved from side to side. Due to her own ignorance of infants, Tamara had developed only the most tentative of relationships with Jennifer. Not that Jennifer objected to something more friendly. She was a happy baby and more than willing to be friends; she had an indiscriminate love of the human race, gurgling and cooing whenever anyone looked her way. But Tamara didn't have the same trust. Jennifer was a mystery to her, and she held her gingerly and fed her only occasionally, leaving the tougher tasks to Rebecca. It was far easier for her to relate to Kevin who could walk, talk, express his emotions and eat with a modicum of civilised manners.

'Tamara, it's good to see you.'

Guy had come into the kitchen with Kevin in his arms and Rebecca beside him. He was a tall, dark-haired man, good-looking and very charming.

'Aunt Tamara,' Kevin pointed out, correcting him.

Guy gave Tamara a grin. 'Pardon me,' he said. 'Aunt Tamara.'

Tamara stood on tip-toe and kissed his cheek. 'It's good to see you, too.'

'When was the last time?' he asked.

Rebecca replied, 'When we visited New York. When Kevin was two.'

'Right,' he nodded. 'I'd forgotten about that.'

They smiled at one another and Tamara knew Guy was remembering the first time they had met. They had both hated one another on sight. He had been furious that she was keeping him from finding Rebecca, and she had been convinced that she was doing the right thing, because she had believed he would destroy her sister's new-found happiness. The antagonism hadn't lasted beyond the wedding, and the wariness between them had waned over the years. Guy was so good to Rebecca that he had earned Tamara's affections, and he in turn had forgiven her the eccentricities that he had found so suspicious and unnerving. Tamara and Guy would never be soul-mates, but their love for Rebecca made them allies.

A small wail made all the adults turn to Jennifer who clearly was unhappy when she was left out of the picture. Guy put Kevin down, strode over to her and lifted her out of the high chair. Her fat toes kicked against his chest as he kissed her cheek. 'How are you, Princess?'

Jennifer grinned and drooled on his suit.

'Still teething, I see,' he said.

Rebecca picked up a teatowel and wiped his lapel. 'I can feel the teeth,' she told her husband proudly. 'They're just about to break through the surface.'

'And I hear you're allergic to cow's milk,' Guy was saying to Jennifer as he tucked her in his arm. 'That's not very nice.'

Kevin tugged at his jacket. 'She cried all the time, Daddy. She kept Mommy up *all night*.'

Guy ruffled Kevin's dark hair. 'That wasn't very nice, was it?'

'No,' replied Kevin stoutly, and when Guy's and Rebecca's eyes met over their son's head, they smiled at one another.

Tamara saw it and felt envy streak through her like a cutting sword. She had never thought she would be jealous of Rebecca. In fact, she had looked down her nose at the type of domestic bliss that her sister found so satisfying. She had thought that it must be boring and unfulfilling; she had never been able to see herself playing the role of the happy housewife. And, while she still wasn't convinced that she would ever be content living Rebecca's days, Tamara was coming to realise that her sister found joy in ways she, Tamara, had not known existed. There was a wonderful serenity to be found in certain moments; when the kitchen smelled of freshly-baking bread, when the baby managed to get a toe in her mouth and then smiled at you as if she had conquered the world, when Kevin, fresh and clean from a bath, sat down next to you and you could smell the sweet scent of him rising from the delicate back of his neck.

Not that Tamara would ever trade those moments for the ones that beckoned to her from the stage. They didn't equal that moment when the collective eye of the audience turned on her and she could feel their interest as a palpable wave on her body. She had always loved the sensation that, through her words and actions, she was reaching out and touching the hearts and minds of strangers. And nothing in the world equalled that triumphant moment of standing on a stage once a performance was over, trembling with exhaustion and dripping with sweat, and hearing the tumultuous adoration of the audience in its thunderous applause.

But, during Tamara's week with Rebecca, she had seen only one side of her sister's life—the side that involved children and cooking, knitting and driving carpools. But there was another side that Tamara had forgotten about, and it was expressed in that very private glance and smile that Rebecca and Guy had shared. The surface serenity of Rebecca's existence was fed by the intimacy and love of two people who are very married, and everything else radiated from that private understanding. Tamara had never known anything like it; she had never been touched by its warmth, its security or its goodness. She had only known a veneer of passion and a careless sort of kindness that comes from a lover whose affections are not truly involved in the act of love.

Tamara had never seen herself as lonely. The term she would have used would be 'independent'. While she had friends and, of course, Rebecca, she was not the sort to cultivate attachments to other people. Those sorts of connections would have hampered her style, infringed on her activities and muddied her single and intense aim of being New York's most famous actress. The result was that she had no one really close to her and no relationship that provided her with stability and caring and tenderness. Not that she needed one, Tamara thought to herself. She had lived this long in perfect happiness all on her own. But still a small ache remained in the vicinity of her heart even when Guy and Rebecca had stopped looking at one another, when Kevin was demanding more attention and it was obvious that Jennifer needed a nappy change. And it stayed with her throughout dinner and into the evening. It didn't even pass when Jake arrived, although the sensation of it was lost in the midst of other, more immediate, emotions.

Jake didn't want to interfere with Guy's first few hours at home after a two-week trip away, so he didn't show up at the McLaren house until about eight that night. His arrival was timed perfectly with the serving of coffee and dessert, and he gave Rebecca a rueful glance. 'I figured you'd be done with dinner.'

'Sure,' Guy said with mock-cynicism.

'I put out an extra muffin for you already,' Rebecca smiled. 'See?'

The family was in the living room, and she pointed towards the antique sideboard. One last blueberry muffin was sitting in isolated splendour on a tray that held a coffee pot, creamer and sugar bowl. Jake gave a slight cough. 'You knew I was coming?'

Rebecca smiled at him. 'Let's just say I knew you couldn't keep away.'

'It's good, Uncle Jake,' Kevin piped up proudly. 'I made it.'

Jake took off his coat, threw it over a chair and picked up the muffin. 'Well, in that case,' he answered, 'I guess I can let my arm get pulled.'

Kevin's small face registered bewilderment. 'Why do you have to pull your arm?'

Guy began explaining, Rebecca poured another cup of coffee and Jake glanced around him. The room was cosy and warm and filled with family things. Jennifer was in her playpen, dressed in a pink terrytowelling sleeper with a large bunny embroidered on the front and was batting at a mobile of wooden animals that hung over her head. Guy was on the floor with Kevin, arranging a set of building blocks into a vast city of winding streets and buildings. Little metal cars dotted the carpet around them. It was a comforting scene, and one that Jake had always enjoyed. He would never have called himself domestic and, while he thought Guy was damned lucky to have found a woman like Rebecca, his heart was not envious. He merely liked the chance that he had to drop into a family setting once in a while. It formed a refreshing counterpoint to a life-style that occasionally grew stale and jaded.

So it was with great pleasure that Jake surveyed the room, and he didn't let the only jarring note in it bother him at all. He was far too fond of Guy and Rebecca to let his dislike of the woman on the couch interfere with his friendship. Therefore, he gave her an amiable nod, noting the blue and purple caftan with the gold threads that she wrapped around her legs and the purple headband that restrained the crinkled mass of her hair. It was a wierd outfit by Jake's standards, but she looked better than she had in the airport. Her face was less pinched and, without the covering of heavy make-up, she looked fresher, less artificial. But she still didn't tempt him, and his first impression of her held firm. Jake didn't find her particularly attractive, he knew the sharpness of her tongue and, besides, he could feel the animosity emanating from her in waves.

'Hello,' he said.

Tamara's nod was frosty.

Jake ignored it, sank down on the floor beside Guy and said to Kevin's delight, 'Hey, can I play?'

Over the movement of coloured blocks and the

roaring of miniature cars being parked in lop-sided garages or being run up ramps that went nowhere, Guy and Jake talked business, re-hashing the two weeks of travel and office com-plications. While they were discussing Guy's appraisal of the crews he had been visiting, Rebecca picked up Jennifer who had started to fuss and sat down on the couch next to Tamara, bouncing the baby gently on her knee. The conversation then turned to football and the relative advantages of the Stampeders over the Ottawa Rough Riders, the Toronto Argonauts and the Edmonton Eskimos.

Football, Tamara thought, eyeing Jake's west-ern-style plaid shirt and jeans with disdain. *Jocks. It figures.*

When the subject of interceptions and running yards had been thoroughly exhausted, Jake turned to Rebecca, saying, 'I took Cordelia out to dinner last night.'

'Where'd you go?'

'That new place downtown where the waiters dress up like Indians.'

Indians, Tamara thought. *God*.

'Was it good?'

'Great steak.'

Steak.

'She sends her love and says she'll be by on the weekend.' Jake suppressed a grin as he thought of Cordelia's other bit of information. He had promised not to mention her boy-friend, Henry, either to Guy or Rebecca; she wanted to tell them herself.

Guy said, 'Maybe she'd like to go sightseeing in the mountains with us. I thought we might take Tamara to Banff now that she's feeling better.'

You wouldn't have thought such innocent words would provoke such a reaction. There was a flurry of motion from both Rebecca and Tamara, an odd exchange of looks and a quick shaking of Rebecca's head to her sister's questioning look.

Guy was mystified. 'You told me she was going to the doctor.'

'She did,' Rebecca answered.

'And isn't she better?' He glanced at Tamara who was now staring down at her entwined hands. 'She looks fine to me.'

Rebecca gave Tamara a helpless, beseeching glance, but the head remained rebelliously bent. 'Tam?'

'Hey,' cheered Jake heartily. 'What is this? A conspiracy?'

The head raised and the blue eyes glared at him, pale sapphires with an angry glint in the centres. 'No conspiracy,' she replied coldly.

Jake felt his amiability slipping. He didn't know why Tamara was capable of lighting the slow fuse of his anger, but there was something about her that just grated on his nerves the wrong way. And, whenever he thought about that meeting in the airport, it rankled the hell out of him. 'Look,' he declared, 'I don't give a damn. You could be pregnant for all I care.'

There was a moment of stunned silence among the adults. Only the sound of Kevin imitating the sound of a car revving its engine filled the void.

Jake felt Guy's eyes resting on him with mystification and Rebecca's shock was palpable. He didn't give a damn that Tamara had lost even the pale colour in her face, but he did regret upsetting his friends. He hadn't wanted to bring his animosity for Tamara out in the open; he had planned to be polite and gracious and a good guest.

'Forget it,' he said, standing up in preparation for leaving.

'But . . . she is,' Rebecca stammered.

Guy sat up straighter. 'What?' he demanded.

With all eyes upon her now, Tamara rose to the occasion. She also stood up, allowing the caftan to fall in heavy folds around her so that only her small bare toes were visible beneath the hem. The light now angled directly on to her, and the orange of her hair and the purple of her headband clashed violently. Jake gaped at her; she seemed taller, far less delicate and powerful in a way he couldn't understand at all. She dominated the room, her chin lifted in a regal fashion, her eyes dared them all to judge her, pity her or censure her in any way. She looked directly at Jake. 'You may not give a damn,' she remarked clearly, 'but the fact is that I am.'

He closed his mouth, swallowed and discovered that he couldn't look away from her. He had never seen anything like it; she seemed to glitter at him in the light, all colours and planes and edges. The coppery-orange strands of her hair melded metallically with the gold threads in the caftan; her cheekbones angled more sharply than he had realised; her chin was pointed.

Jake still didn't like her, but for a second he actually admired her. Then he shook off the feeling, and the room swung back into focus. Guy and Rebecca were staring at the two of them; even the children were quiet as if something strange or momentous had occurred. He felt the sudden urge to defuse the situation and play it down. He forced himself to relax, sat down in a chair near by and nonchalantly put a booted ankle over his knee. When he spoke, the tone of his voice was worldly and knowledgeable as if unmarried pregnant women were the standard fare of his days.

'No kidding,' he drawled.

CHAPTER FIVE

THE rest of the evening was anti-climactic after that. The room came back to life as if the play enacted within it were over, the curtain had come down and the audience, held in thrall by the enmity of the protagonists, had been released from the spell. Jennifer started to fuss, and Kevin, accidentally knocking over a carefully erected tower of blocks, began to cry. The children required attention and, once Guy had got over his shock and the situation had been explained, the conversation about Tamara's condition covered the same ground that she and Rebecca had traversed already. There were no new arguments and no new answers to a dilemma that pitted logic against emotion, reason against something unknown that Tamara could neither understand nor define. Jake didn't stay very long after that, and Tamara went to bed soon after he had gone. She was exhausted, confused and angry, a combination that kept her up for hours despite a numbing fatigue. She crawled into bed, convinced that she would drop off to sleep immediately, only to discover that her mind refused to stop churning. The evening kept coming back like the replay of a bad movie.

It was during these long hours when she lay in bed and stared up at the dark ceiling that Tamara realised she was going to have the baby. It was a decision that frightened her immensely, and she curled up into a tight ball under the covers, her arms wrapped around herself, her knees drawn up to her chest. She shivered and shook and cursed herself for being a sentimental idiot; she muttered to the stillness of the room and wondered aloud what right she had to bring a child into the world. In her head, she listed her flaws and her liabilities, and the list was long and detailed. When she tried to come up with some sterling qualities and assets, the total was abysmally small. She had nothing to offer a baby but herself, and Tamara wasn't sure that was enough.

She was selfish, she thought, egotistical, impatient and demanding. She didn't know the first thing about making sacrifices or yielding to the needs of someone else. And she hadn't a clue how to be a mother. Rebecca might be a marvellous example, but Tamara knew that she would never have Rebecca's style of mothering. They were too different and, besides, her sister was married: she would be a single parent. And there was nothing in her childhood that would give her any hints. Even before her parents' divorce, Tamara and Martine had been at loggerheads. Much as she hated to admit it, Tamara understood that she and her mother were similar in personality and temperament. Of course, she had loved her father to distraction, but that hadn't meant anything, had it? Nothing, she thought with bitterness. Nothing.

Tamara turned over and pushed the subject of her father away. She wouldn't think about that; she hadn't in years. Life, she had found, was much simpler that way. Instead, she concentrated on the immensity of her decision, her hand placed on the deceiving flatness of her stomach, and tried to understand why. The odds were against her; she couldn't imagine having a baby in her run-down Manhattan apartment; she had no idea what she would do for money; and the idea of taking care of a child and pursuing her career was crushing. It simply didn't make sense. It was crazy. She must be crazy. Something inside of her was making her crazy.

'Hell!' she muttered into the darkness and turned over once again, plumping the pillow under her cheek and pulling the covers up over her shoulders. It wasn't just something within her; she knew that. Exterior forces were playing on her. There was the serenity of this house and Rebecca's happiness. There were Jennifer's toothless smiles and fat little legs. And there was Jake. If she never told anyone else, Tamara had to admit it to herself. Jake and that goddamn supercilious attitude of his had tipped the scales and pushed her over into the craziest decision of her life.

Tamara had tried to ignore him for most of the evening. She had gone from disdain of him, to active dislike, and then to positive hatred in a very short period of time. Everything about Jake set her nerves on edge. She didn't like the way he dressed, the way he talked or the subject of his conversation. She had planned on tolerating him for Guy's and Rebecca's sake, but the moment she had seen him standing in the entrance way of the living room, his eyes passing over her as if she barely existed, her tolerance level had sunk to an all-time low. Jake irked her and she knew why. It wasn't just his clothes or his external characteristics that bothered her; it was the fact that he was so indifferent to her as a woman. Tamara was used to attracting men; she could do it just by a sideways glance, a small smile or a clever remark. It didn't matter that she wouldn't have taken Jake if he were the last man on earth; it was just that she would have preferred to have the power herself to make the choice.

And when his indifference had coupled with that lazy amusement at her expense, Tamara had felt the rage rising within her like a geyser. She could see that Jake thought he had her number. All through the conversation with Guy and Rebecca, he had smiled knowingly. He didn't think she would keep the baby; in fact, his smile had clearly revealed what he thought Tamara's protestations were all about. He didn't credit her with any emotion other than a crying need to be the centre of attention. His attitude had been written across his broad, handsome face as if it were inscribed there with a sharp pen. He thought her self-centred, promiscuous and not a little stupid. It was clear that Jake was very familiar with a certain kind of woman; the kind who sleeps around with no discrimination, isn't responsible and is forced to get rid of the unwanted consequences. He had judged Tamara, classified her and then dismissed her, and she had hated it. She was quite desperate to prove Jake wrong; never in her life had Tamara been a 'type' or predictable, and she didn't want to start now.

This was no good reason, she knew, for having a baby, but it was mixed in with all the other emotions tugging and pulling at her. She had swayed between common sense and sentimentality, between reason and irrationality, not understanding much of it and miserable with not knowing what to do. Jake had unwittingly pushed her in the direction that she was least expected to go. The satisfaction she would get from being different and perverse was minor compared to the reality of having and caring for a baby, but the anticipation of the shock Jake would receive from her decision gave Tamara a fair amount of pleasure. It would have been even more perfect, she thought as she turned over once again, if she could see his reaction. She imagined several scenarios and fell asleep to the nicest of them—the one in which he admitted, grudgingly and with admiration, that he hadn't really understood Tamara Clark in the first place.

'If the government would only loosen up on foreign investment,' Guy was saying, 'the increase in business would be substantial.'

'Yeah,' Jake agreed. They had chewed over this issue for years. The Canadian government had been making it difficult for US companies to invest in Canadian energy development since the mid-'seventies. It was a policy that was supposed to inspire national pride and give incentive to Canadian companies to invest in their own resources. The trouble was—there weren't enough of them to go around. And, although business was good for McLaren & DeBlais Associates, it would have been a lot better if they could have laid their hands on some lucrative American contracts.

'A rising interest rate is going to put a damper on things.'

Jake nodded again and bit into his pastrami sandwich. He and Guy regularly took Friday lunch together. It was a time they had set apart to meet and talk leisurely about the week's business. Despite the fact that they worked in the same office, they were often so busy that they rarely had a chance to share ideas. So the Friday lunches had become an institution. The setting hadn't mattered particularly; they chose to meet in a restaurant on the first floor of their office building. The decor was strictly utilitarian but the food was palatable and the service was quick and efficient.

'Anyway, the accountant wants to come in and look at the books next Wednesday, but I have a meeting with Brenner at Aviation Express. Would you be able to see him?'

'I think so.'

There was a comfortable silence then as both men ate their sandwiches. They were, from a visual standpoint, an interesting contrast in colour and style. Guy, who was dark and slender, tended towards dark shades in suits; navy blues, deep greys and the charcoal he was wearing today with its faint white stripe. His jacket was always conservative in cut, and his ties had small patterns on them. Jake was somewhat more flamboyant, although his clothes never stepped beyond the bounds of good taste. He favoured light colours; beige, pale greys, slate blue, and he liked a western cut with a defined yoke in the back and top-stitched pockets. And no matter how well-pressed his suits were, Jake had the slightest tendency to look rumpled. It had something to do with his size, the powerful build of his muscles and the shagginess of his blond hair.

'Want to come over for dinner on Saturday?'

Jake shook his head. 'Thanks for the invitation, but I've already got a date.'

Guy lifted an eyebrow. 'And who is the lucky woman?'

'You don't know her. A blonde. Her name is Helen.'

'A blonde named Helen.' Guy mused for a moment. 'I know a blonde named Helen—she's executive secretary at Fokker Aeronautics.'

Jake speared a french fry. 'That's her.'

Guy leaned back in his chair and appraised his friend. 'Isn't that going a little too far—even for you?'

'What's that supposed to mean?'

'From what I hear Helen is capable of giving you a not-so-rare social disease.'

'She's not that bad—she went out with a friend of mine and wouldn't come across.'

'Which friend?'

'O'Hara.'

'Jesus, Jake, no woman would come across for O'Hara.'

'Why? He's okay.'

'Rebecca says he's so slimy he gives her the creeps.'

'Rebecca only likes the wholesome type.'

Guy grinned. 'Like me?'

Jake grinned back. 'They don't make 'em any more wholesome, pal.' There was a short moment of silence and his grin turned slightly rueful. 'All right, she is a bit of a tart.'

'So why go out with her?'

Jake shrugged. 'Maybe my tastes incline in that direction.'

'Maybe,' Guy said with a knowing look, 'you're getting desperate. Maybe you've gone through all the decent and attractive women in town.'

'It's an occupational hazard,' Jake replied. 'The supply can't keep up with my demand.'

'Still no hankering for marriage?'

'Hell, no. Anyway,' he added in a joking voice, 'the only woman I'd want to marry is your mother and she won't wait for me to get through my interminable adolescence.'

Guy smiled and then turned serious. 'Speaking of Cordelia . . .' he began.

Jake took another bite of his sandwich. 'Mmmm?'

'Have you heard the latest?'

Jake decided that discretion was the better part of valour. 'The latest what?'

'She's got a boy-friend.'

'No kidding!'

'So I'm afraid your hopes are in vain.'

Guy's voice was light, but there was something in his face that made Jake lean forward. 'Hey, that doesn't upset you, does it?'

'It's funny,' Guy said, 'but somehow it makes my father's death seem that much more real. Oh, I know he died over three years ago, and I never thought that my mother should be alone for the rest of her life, but another man taking his place makes the loss much more . . . irrevocable.' He gave a short, embarrassed laugh. 'I guess that's the word I want—irrevocable. He isn't ever going to come back, I realised that when I heard about Henry. Not that I begrudge my mother a male friend, but it's hard to imagine another man sitting at my father's place at the table.'

Jake looked sympathetic, but he couldn't help wondering if Guy realised just how many of Franklin's privileges Henry had already usurped.

Guy took a deep breath. 'It's part of growing up, I guess. Accepting the death of a parent and understanding that nothing stays the same. Not that I'd say a word to Cordelia, of course. I just let her know how delighted I was and now she's invited us over to meet Henry.'

'You don't have to worry about your mother; she's got a good head on her shoulders. I'll bet Henry's a great guy.'

Guy lifted his beer. 'I hope so.' He paused and then added as he took a sip, 'Cordelia and Tamara really got along.'

'Oh?' answered Jake with disinterest.

'You two haven't hit it off, have you?'

'She's okay.'

'Look, Jake, I know Rebecca tried to cram Tam down your throat.'

'It isn't that. She just doesn't appeal to me.'

'You haven't been to our place in a couple of weeks,' Guy accused gently. 'Rebecca's been wondering why you haven't come by, Kevin has been asking for you and . . . hell, even I miss you. Kevin and I haven't had a good block-building session in days.'

'I'm sorry,' Jake declared, leaning back in his chair and shifting uncomfortably. 'I dislike her. She rubs me up the wrong way. I don't know why, but she does.'

'She's different. I didn't like her when I first met her either.'

'And she doesn't like me,' Jake went on. 'We have a mutual antipathy. Look, there's something about her that makes the hair on the back of my neck rise up. She's too slick, she's got a hard edge to her. Her clothes hurt my eyes and any woman with a tongue like that should be shut away for life.'

Guy couldn't help laughing. 'She isn't all that bad.'

'The answer is no. Besides she's too damned skinny for me.' His final words were a dismissal of the subject of Tamara. Jake beckoned to the waiter, asked for another beer and, turning back to the table, was just about to launch into a discussion of his latest squash game, when Guy spoke.

'She won't be for long.'

Jake blinked. 'Won't be what?'

'Skinny. She's decided to go through with the pregnancy.'

Jake blinked again. 'You're kidding.'

Guy sighed. 'I wish I was.'

Jake felt an anger stir deep within him. He had no idea where the anger came from; it had no logical source, but he couldn't help the way it moved, imprinting itself over other emotions and taking hold of him with a grasping force. 'What the hell does she want with a kid? She doesn't have any money, she doesn't know who the father is, she can't even give it a decent home.'

'She says she wants it.'

'I don't think she has a right to have a kid.'

Guy was surprised at Jake's vehemence. 'That's a pretty strong statement.'

'Children are a responsibility,' Jake stated in a forceful rush. 'They need love and caring and attention and . . .'

'Hey,' said Guy, 'you don't have to tell me about it. Both Rebecca and I have laid it all out for her, but she insists that having the baby is what she wants to do. We're going to sponsor her so that she can get landed immigrant status here. That way her medical care will be covered by the provincial plan.'

Jake was barely listening to Guy's last words. He was shaking his head back and forth. The unaccountable anger was growing and threatening to blossom out as a fully-fledged rage. 'Some people are goddamned selfish.'

'It's her choice,' Guy returned, a little bemused at Jake's obvious anger.

'It shouldn't be,' Jake growled with a conviction born of fury. 'A woman like that shouldn't have that kind of a choice.'

They parted after that; Jake had an appointment and Guy had to go back to the office. Jake pushed Tamara and her pregnancy out of his mind. He had better things to think about. He played a vicious game of squash that night, and spent Saturday morning paying bills. In the afternoon, he took his jeep to a co-op garage and tinkered with it for a few hours. By the time he returned back to his apartment, it was time to get ready for his date with Helen. He showered, shaved, brushed his hair, thinking that it needed a cut again, and spent ten minutes deciding which suit to wear. He finally selected the cream cord suit, a pale blue shirt and a darker blue tie.

'Not bad,' he said to his image in the mirror over his dresser. He grinned at himself as he thought about the evening to come. He wasn't the slightest bit worried about Helen; he had a good idea how the night would end. The question was—would it be in his place or hers? Jake looked around his bedroom, wondered whether he should change the sheets and then shrugged.

They were clean enough and, if she didn't like dark blue with a white stripe, that was her problem. Still, he did make the effort to neaten the apartment a bit, picking up the newspapers in the living room, the files on his desk and the clutter in the kitchen.

Jake thought he had a pretty spectacular place. It had three bedrooms, a living room with a spacious expanse of glass facing the mountains and an ultra-modern kitchen. Most of his friends had predicted that he would go the macho route in home decoration; leather and tweed, glass and chrome, but Jake had surprised them. The colours in his apartment were soft shades of blue and grey, the textures were velvet and plush, the lines of the furniture slightly curved. He had no idea what had moved him to fill his apartment with objects that had a feminine as well as masculine touch. He only knew that his taste had gravitated towards things that were soft and gentle.

He picked up Helen at her apartment, took her to dinner and then a show at the Jubilee Center. Afterwards, they went back to his place and made love until about one o'clock in the morning. Although Helen wanted to stay the night, Jake insisted on taking her home. He gave her a lingering kiss at her door, said he would call her soon, and shrugged with an angry sort of relief when he got back to the car. There was nothing intrinsically wrong with Helen. She was pretty, willing to please and determined to make a good impression. Her technique in bed had been faultless; she had even made an effort to be affectionate. No, the problem was his. In the midst of listening to her prattle, of kissing her eager mouth, of exploring that pale, pliable body, he had been thinking of someone else.

Jake drove home too fast, exceeding the speed limit by tens of miles. He had to brake hard when he parked the jeep in its spot, and he slammed the door when he got out. Not even the soothing atmosphere of his apartment gave him any serenity. He sat down in the most comfortable chair in the living room, the one with the winged sides and the matching ottoman, tried to read a few magazines and discovered that he couldn't concentrate. Then, after tearing the sheets off the bed and changed them completely, he tried to sleep. That didn't work either. He had had everything that night that a man wanted—good food, nice entertainment, companionship and sex, a combination that usually had him smiling and asleep within seconds. Tonight, however, he tossed and turned, felt alternately hot and cold, and kicked covers on and off in an endless and frustrating cycle of insomnia.

Jake couldn't, for the life of him, get Tamara Clark out of his head. She jeered at him, sneered at him, appraised him and laughed at him. Her face appeared to him against a backdrop of colours—pink, purple, royal blue, black—her eyes were like pale sapphires, and her hair glowed the orange of a sunset. He could hear the sound of her voice and could recall, in perfect detail, that moment when she had dominated the McLarens' living room, growing before his eyes until she had a stature that surpassed that of any woman he had known.

Jake tried to shake that off; she was an actress after all, and probably had any number of strange tricks up her sleeve. But he couldn't shake her out of his mind, and she clung there, stubborn as a limpet, until he finally fell asleep at about five o'clock in the morning out of sheer exhaustion. But his sleep was restless and, when he woke six hours later, he was drained and tired, the pounding of a headache starting to drum in his temples. He felt bad-tempered and out of sorts; he felt as if something unpleasant had turned his ordinarily content life upside down and inside out. He ran his fingers impatiently through the shaggy strands of his hair and cursed out loud.

'Witch,' he said, his teeth clenching together. 'Goddamned, crazy witch.'

Winter in Calgary came quickly as the arctic winds blew down from the north, their strength increasing in the turbulence over the Rockies, and then swept down the foothills to slant the prairie grasses flat against the cold earth. There was little snow, and the sky stayed clear and blue almost every day but, in the distance, when the clouds had risen over the mountains, Tamara could see that the snow-caps covering their peaks were increasing day by day, their bottom edge lowering like the hems of white skirts to the tree-line.

The cold and the diamond-hard quality of the air seemed to suit her as she passed out of the first three months of her pregnancy and into her fourth and fifth month. Her extreme fatigue disappeared and she stopped vomiting. She had a regime so healthy, she referred to it as disgusting, but obediently swallowed vitamin pills and drank glasses of milk. She often went for walks around the neighbourhood, feeling the wind whip colour into her face and pushing Jennifer who was bundled up like an Eskimo in her stroller. The concavity of her abdomen vanished and the angularity of her hip-bones softened as the pregnancy began to fill her out. Her breasts—'if I get a mosquito bite on my chest, then I have three' —continued to swell until she actually began to fit some of the maternity tops that Rebecca had found for her.

Although she was taken on several sightseeing tours of the mountains and Calgary itself, Tamara had little interest in the city or the loveliness of Banff, Jasper and Lake Louise. It wasn't that the mountains weren't grand and awe-inspiring or the lake wasn't blue beyond imagining; it was simply that she was most comfortable in the security of a domestic setting. This shocked her at first; that, and the fact that she had taken up knitting. 'I don't believe this,' she complained to Rebecca who only smiled. 'I feel bovine. I'm turning into a cow.' Tamara didn't start with the standard scarf in easy-to-knit garter stitch. She toiled over intricate and delicate sweaters that would fit the tiniest baby. The yarn she used was always soft and pastel in colour; the patterns had star shapes in the yokes, tiny rows of popcorn stitching and minute buttonholes. They were pretty when they were done and completely impractical considering the uncivilised habits of infants but, for some reason, she loved making them.

She fitted easily and unobtrusively into the rhythms of the household which, in itself, was astonishing when she remembered what an obtrusive person she generally had been. Perhaps the years of frenetic pace, the constant energy to maintain that intense ambition and the months of illness had simply taken the starch out of her. It was a thought that would have bothered the Tamara of earlier times, but now she accepted it with a surprising amount of graciousness. In fact, she had come to look on her stay with Rebecca and her pregnancy as a time when she could sit back, catch her breath and try to sort through the complicated strands of her life. She had never had time to do that before; she had never even given herself a second to actually think.

It was during this period of time that Tamara began to realise that one of the reasons why she wanted the baby was because she was quite desperate to love someone. Her ability to care about anyone other than herself had shrivelled up during the years when she was alone. With her own well-being first, last and foremost in her mind, she had ignored the needs of others. There was a part of her inside that felt as dry and wrinkled as an old pea left too long in a dusty bin. It hurt when it rattled around her, rubbing at places that were sore and empty and wanting. A lot of people might accuse her of having a baby because she needed to be loved, but Tamara could see that love with infants was strictly a one-way street. Jennifer soaked in her parents' love like a sponge and, although their efforts were rewarded by smiles and happy responses, it would be years before Jennifer would be old enough to know how to love in return. No, there was something in Tamara that needed to care about the child lying so quiescent inside of her, its motion only discernible as the faintest of flutterings.

The days rolled by slowly and calmly. Guy and Rebecca went out occasionally and entertained rarely. Cordelia came by, but Henry had moved in with her and they were busy planning a winter trip to the Bahamas. Her visits were short and rushed, but always invigorating. Tamara liked Cordelia's humour, down-to-earth pragmatism and tolerance. Cordelia, in turn, enjoyed Tamara's exoticism and experience. And now that she was in the midst of a love affair, she needed the occasional confidante. Tamara would never forget a conversation they had one afternoon when Rebecca had taken the baby upstairs to change her nappy. It was then that Cordelia had confided in her as if they two were experienced women of the world and Rebecca still an innocent child.

'Mirrors,' Cordelia had said. 'Have you ever known a man who likes mirrors?'

Tamara stared at her blankly. 'Mirrors?'

Cordelia blushed to the roots of her styled hair.

She was wearing a long strand of pearls, and she fingered these nervously. 'You know what I mean.'

'No, I . . . *oh*, I get you.' Tamara couldn't help smiling and then added, 'Not Henry.'

'Franklin wasn't like this. He was more . . . conservative, I guess. It wasn't that we didn't have a good sex life. We did; it was very satisfactory, but Henry seems to have more . . .' she cleared her throat '. . . imagination.'

Tamara had slept with too many men to think that Henry's proclivities with reflection were odd or perverted. Still, it boggled her mind to think of sweet, little Henry and mirrors. He was a small man with a neatly trimmed white van dyke beard, a narrow white fringe over his ears and a taste in flamboyant bow-ties.

'A lot of men like mirrors,' she reassured soothingly.

The pearls looped around Cordelia's hand and up over her fingers. 'Well, I wondered . . .'

Tamara could see that Cordelia still wasn't sure that Henry's needs were normal and acceptable. 'It's when he gets into whips,' she said, 'that you have to start worrying.'

'Whips?'

'And chains.'

'Chains . . . good heavens,' Cordelia echoed breathlessly. 'You must be joking.'

Tamara solemnly shook her head. 'You wouldn't believe the weirdos out there.'

'I guess that mirrors aren't so bad then.'

Tamara leaned forward and patted Cordelia on

the hand. 'Enjoy yourself,' she said. 'There aren't too many men of Henry's age who can manage it, much less do it in front of a mirror.'

Tamara rarely saw Jake during this period and, when she did, they were unfailingly polite with one another. Both Rebecca and Guy were aware of the animosity between them and were careful to keep them apart. There was no more talk of matchmaking or romance; their mutual dislike had ended that and the pregnancy had cemented it. In fact, there was an unspoken agreement among the three adults in the McLaren house that Tamara was out of bounds as far as men were concerned and she, who had never been celibate in her life, didn't mind it at all. The sexual side of herself had yielded to the maternal; she was far too involved in the changes in her body and in her increasingly active unborn child to be the least bit interested in the opposite sex.

Jake, on the other hand, didn't follow a course of abstinence and, whenever Tamara caught the edges of a conversation about Jake between Guy and Rebecca, there was a note of worry in their voices. She gathered that the women he was now dating were far less appealing than his former girl-friends and he changed them even more quickly than he had in the past. Rebecca was concerned about the state of Jake's happiness and insisted that this turnover in female companionship was indicative of a deep restlessness on Jake's part. Guy didn't like it, but he shrugged it off as a phase. He didn't believe that any woman in the world was capable of making Jake settle down.

Tamara didn't much care and, as time went by, she found it easier and easier to ignore Jake's existence. When he came to the house, she often didn't leave her bedroom, but sat in the rocking-chair, knitting yet another small sweater. From her window, she could see him arrive and then leave, his shoulders even broader in his heavy suede coat, his blond hair hidden beneath a fur hat. He was a big man, but in the distance from her window, he appeared smaller and, when his jeep disappeared down the driveway, its exhaust a white plume in the chill, she forgot about him almost immediately. There were so many more important things to think about.

More and more, Tamara was lulled into an unusual serenity. The days were quiet, the evenings were broken up by Guy's arrival home from work, and the nights were peaceful. By the time she had reached the beginning of her sixth month of pregnancy, she was napping in the afternoon and sleeping a solid eight hours or more until morning. Her gynaecologist announced her sound and healthy, and a sonogram showed a foetus that was normal. So normal, in fact, that it was already sucking its thumb. Tamara worried about tooth development, and Rebecca suggested a dummy. Then they both laughed when they realised that they were talking about a baby that wouldn't be born for four months.

Christmas came and went; Tamara baby-sat on

New Year's Eve, insisting that Guy and Rebecca go out and have a good time. Their marriage was so companionable that it was obvious that Rebecca and Guy rarely needed other people, but Tamara wasn't sure this was healthy. She offered to baby-sit more often, not quite understanding Rebecca's reluctance. It wasn't until one January night that Tamara realised that something was not quite right between Rebecca and Guy. Of course, she had known that their marriage wasn't idyllic; they argued occasionally and bickered over household affairs, but she had never seen them really fight and had marvelled at them. She had thought they were wonderful and that their marriage proved the impossible. If she hadn't got up that night to get a drink of water, she would never have discovered that, beneath the surface, Guy and Rebecca were quite capable of being as angry and as vicious with one another as any other couple.

The sounds of their fighting were so loud that they came right up the stairwell to Tamara who was standing in the carpeted corridor, dressed only in her nightgown, her toes bare against the plush. The anger in their voices shocked her, and she stood stock-still, her back pressed against the cold wall.

'Have you asked Tamara yet?' Guy was saying.

Rebecca's voice was low. 'No.'

'Why not?'

'You know why not.'

'Damn it,' Guy returned angrily, 'you're being selfish.'

'You're the one being selfish,' Rebecca threw back. 'They're your children, too.'

'That doesn't mean I have to be with them all the time. They're healthy, well-adjusted kids. They can live without me, and you, for a couple of weeks.'

'I don't want to go. I don't want to leave them.'

'You're not abandoning them. I'm sure Tamara would take good care of them.'

'You don't understand.'

'Oh, yes, I do. I understand perfectly. After all, we've been over this ground half a dozen times before. I need a holiday and I'd like to have it *with* you and *without* the children. I'm not asking for a lot.'

There was a faint tone of hysteria in Rebecca's voice. 'The children need me.'

'They need a caretaker. Jennifer needs someone to change her nappy and give her a bottle. Kevin needs someone to feed him dinner, read him a story at night and tuck him in.'

'They need love, too.'

The clenching of Guy's teeth was an almost audible sound. 'Rebecca, you're only leaving them for two or three weeks at the most. Tamara's love will be sufficient for that amount of time. Doesn't the idea of a few weeks in the sun appeal to you at all?'

'Of course it does, but don't you think the children would also enjoy . . .'

'They'd love it, but *we* need to get away. You and me alone together. And I need to get away

from the office and the house and the everyday
responsibilities. It's been a hard year; you know
that. I've been working like crazy.'

'I don't want to leave them. You know how I
feel about leaving. My father . . .'

Tamara could tell by the irritated tone of Guy's
voice that this was a familiar and often disputed
territory. 'I'm not your father and you're not your
mother. We are not "leaving" them for ever. We
are simply getting away for a few weeks, just the
two of us.'

Rebecca was pleading now, and Tamara could
imagine her twisting her hands together in agi-
tation. It was a typical Rebecca response. 'The
idea of it makes me feel frantic inside. You don't
understand; I get panicky.'

There was a moment of silence and then Guy
said wearily, 'Don't I count at all, Rebecca?'

'You do!'

'Sometimes I doubt it.'

A teary sound. 'Guy . . .'

But there were heavy footsteps coming up the
stairs and Tamara slipped back into her room,
shutting the door silently behind her. She was
trembling as if she had stood between Guy and
Rebecca, absorbing their anger and frustration,
buffeted by strong emotions and a tension
sprung so tight that her own hands were
clenched together, the knuckles white and
strained.

The next morning, all signs of a marital battle had
been removed. If Tamara hadn't actually heard

the angry words being exchanged, she would have never known from Guy's and Rebecca's demeanour that they weren't the world's happiest couple. There was the usual bustle at breakfast with Kevin talking while he ate his Cheerios and Jennifer bubbling her way through mouthfuls of peaches and rice cereal. Guy gave Rebecca her customary kiss good-bye, but Tamara wondered if they had slept in the same bed that night together. Now that she knew the truth, she felt a cool undercurrent beneath the seemingly affectionate surface of their relationship.

Of course, it wasn't in Rebecca's nature to say anything. Tamara knew her sister better than she knew anyone else, and she was well aware that Rebecca had always kept things to herself. It was hard for her to express pain or hurt or unhappiness. As an adolescent she had buried her miseries under an avalanche of food, developing an alarming obesity by the time she was fifteen. Since meeting Guy, she had lost that need to eat whenever her world went awry, but her basic personality hadn't changed at all. She suffered in silence, and it took a hyper-sensitive observer to perceive the suffering.

Tamara waited until Guy had gone, Kevin had been picked up by the carpool and Jennifer was busy in her playpen. She sat down at the table in the kitchen, poured herself a tall glass of milk and went in for the attack.

'Do you know why our father skipped out?' she asked.

Rebecca stood motionless, her hand stilled in

its motion as she reached up into a cupboard for a mixing bowl. 'Skipped out?' she echoed.

'Because Martine tried to control him all the time.' It wasn't the whole truth—Tamara would never tell anyone that—but it was convenient enough for her purposes. 'Because he was tired of being told what to do, how to act, and the best way to run his life. Because she didn't give him a chance to be spontaneous or have a moment's fun.'

Rebecca slowly turned around to face her. 'You heard us fighting last night, didn't you?'

'I didn't mean to,' Tamara confessed. 'But I couldn't help it.'

Rebecca leaned back against the counter, her face wary. The sun caught in the mahogany strands of her hair and turned them a dark red. 'Guy doesn't understand how I feel.'

Tamara had thought out her strategy the night before. She knew it was going to be painful, but she also knew that it was the quickest and most efficient means to a positive end. She shrugged lightly, took a nonchalant sip of her milk and said in a cool and disdainful voice, 'Grow up, Rebecca.'

It was as if she had wielded a whip; Rebecca flinched and stiffened. 'What do you mean?'

'You're full of adolescent hang-ups and childish fears. So our father walked out. You know damn well that your taking a vacation with Guy isn't the same thing at all.'

'I know it rationally but emotionally, I feel . . .'

'You're controlling him; you're trying to limit

his freedom. Martine did it and look where it got her.'

'Guy isn't going to divorce me.'

'Trusting Rebecca.' Tamara saw it was time to twist the knife. 'Maybe he'll find a girl-friend who will give him a vacation at home.'

Now Rebecca was starting to get angry. As Tamara had known since childhood, her sister had a slow fuse and a spark that didn't ignite easily. It took a lot of provocation to get Rebecca mad. 'You're interfering,' cried Rebecca accusingly.

'I can't tell you the number of men who've had a little fling with me because their wives didn't make them happy.'

'Guy isn't like other men.'

'Then he's not human.'

'You're trying to make me feel insecure!'

'Right,' Tamara agreed. 'I'm trying to scare the complacent pants off you. You're lucky, Becks, real lucky. You happened to marry one of the nicest men I've ever met. Don't ruin a good thing.'

'Our family was such a mess,' Rebecca said with a note of pleading in her voice. 'I always felt as if no one cared, as if everyone was always leaving, as if . . .'

'You're not really afraid that the kids will feel abandoned; the truth is that *you'll* feel empty and lost without them. You have a wonderful home here, Becks. It's serene and quiet and soothing. The trouble is that you're letting it take over your whole life. And you're going to lose your husband in the process.'

Rebecca's hands stopped clenching the counter. 'I think you're obnoxious,' she declared coldly.

Tamara soothed down the mass of her hair. 'The truth is rarely pleasant.'

'And I don't want to talk about this any more.'

Tamara gave another shrug. She was particularly good at shrugging. With one lift and droop of her shoulders she was capable of expressing a range of emotions—from distaste to indifference to a smug superiority. In one play that she had been in, the climactic moment had hinged on a mere shrug of her shoulders, and Tamara had practised for hours to get it right.

'That's fine with me.'

'It's none of your business anyway.'

She was also good at lifting her eyebrows as if to say—Really?

'I mean it, Tam. I don't want you telling me what to do or implying that Guy is going to be unfaithful. You have no right to do that.'

'Just don't say I didn't warn you.'

The look Rebecca threw at Tamara as she walked out of the kitchen was loaded with pure venom. It had the effect of making Tamara smile to herself and cheerfully gulp down the rest of her milk. She knew the exact train of events that would follow. Rebecca would be furious for an hour or so and then she would cool off. Anger had always had a way of making Rebecca mulish, but she was usually reasonable once she had simmered down. During this second phase, common sense would rear its pragmatic head, and she would begin to wonder if Tamara was right. She would then apologise to Tamara for calling her obnoxious. The third phase would entail hours of soul-searching and deep thinking. The fourth phase would be agreement. Tamara hadn't spent her first seventeen years living with Rebecca for nothing. Her sister was as transparent as a sheet of glass. She had been malleable at ten and she was just as malleable at thirty-one.

All it had taken, Tamara thought comfortably as she learned back in the chair, was a smidgen of duplicity, a small amount of manipulation and a tiny application of psychology. And it was nice to know that her dramatic abilities hadn't grown rusty from disuse. She had used just the right amount of needling anger to make Rebecca reach the proper level of indignation. Not bad, Tamara decided, not bad for one used actress, six months pregnant.

CHAPTER SIX

Guy and Rebecca left early on a Thursday morning for a three-week trip to Mexico. Tamara was left with a full freezer and refrigerator, a long list of instructions, enough telephone numbers to cover any emergency and plenty of cash in case of a crisis or two. Rebecca had spent the week before her vacation stocking the house with food. She filled not only the kitchen cabinets but also several shelves in the basement with canned goods and baby food. Then she arranged a daily delivery of milk, butter and bread. Despite Guy's assertion that they had already had enough food to last a year, Rebecca had been determined that, if nothing else, Tamara and the children wouldn't starve. And, because Tamara didn't drive and couldn't participate in the carpool that drove Kevin and three other children to kindergarten, Rebecca spent hours on the phone co-ordinating the other mothers. *And*, just in case Tamara wanted to go out, she bought taxi chits from a local company.

'And there's always Jake,' she reminded Tamara as she re-packed her bags for the fifth time. Rebecca was in a frenzy about packing, changing her mind so many times over what she would bring that Guy had finally locked himself in his den.

'Jake who?' Tamara asked innocently. She was lying across Rebecca's and Guy's bed watching, with amusement, the increasing proliferation of blouses, skirts, shorts, slacks and dresses.

'Really, Tam. If anything goes wrong, you're to call Jake. His number is . . .'

Tamara sighed. 'On the pad beside the phone in the kitchen.'

Rebecca went on without missing a beat. 'I do wish Cordelia was in town. It would make me feel a lot better if she were.'

'She and Henry are having an orgy in the Bahamas.'

'An orgy!'

Tamara smiled at her. 'Metaphorically speaking, that is. It would appear that Henry has an extremely healthy sex drive.'

Rebecca folded a blouse, stared at it for a moment and then, shaking her head, put it to one side. 'Don't let Guy hear you say that. He's been very good about Henry, but it still bothers him a bit.'

Tamara plumped the pillow behind her head. 'It's the old Oedipus complex on the rampage.'

Rebecca had picked up a dress and was studying it. 'What about this one?' she asked with a frown of concern. 'Do you think the long sleeves will make it too hot?'

'I like the red one better.'

'The red one . . . the red one. Well, I guess so.' Rebecca put down one dress and picked up another. 'Anyway, don't forget about Jake.'

'I won't.'

'I know you don't like him, but he's wonderful in an emergency.'

'I'm not going to have any.'

'Tam, please. Promise me you'll get in touch with him.'

'Cross my heart.' It was their old, childhood routine, and Tamara lifted her arms and crossed them over her breast. Not that she had any intention of ever getting in touch with Jake. The house would have to burn down before she did that.

'I'm serious. If anything goes wrong . . .'

'Nothing will,' Tamara said soothingly. 'Everything is going to be perfect. Now, stop worrying and have a good time. The children and I will be fine.'

And short of true disaster such as fire, accident, tornado or cyclone, Tamara couldn't think of a problem that she would be unable to solve on her own. She knew the children's routine, and they were genuinely easy to take care of. The worst thing she would have to combat would be boredom; theirs and hers. And to ward off that, Tamara had started to delve into the books in the den, and Rebecca had gone to a toy store and stocked up on colouring books, crayons, new baby toys and simple board games. Tamara was to dole them out one by one whenever a situation arose which demanded a novelty for the purposes of distraction.

No, she couldn't see anything happening that wasn't predictable or unusual, so Tamara shook her head and, using a tone that was utterly fearless and utterly confident, added in a voice designed to reassure, 'I don't want you to think about us at all. We're going to be just fine by ourselves.'

Famous last words.

The day of Guy's and Rebecca's departure went along beautifully. Jennifer never seemed to notice that her mother was missing at all. She allowed Tamara to bathe her with a minimum of splashing and fuss, ate her lunch of puréed lamb and carrots as if it were a gourmet's delight and slept like an angel for three hours in the afternoon. Tamara napped along with her for a short period and then read a mystery for two hours. Kevin arrived home from school, watched an hour of Sesame Street and obediently sat down at the dinner table. He didn't seem to be hungry, but then Tamara didn't believe in forcing food down a child's throat. She had far too vivid memories of Martine threatening dire punishments if she didn't eat her cooked carrots or spinach or peas. So she didn't start worrying until after Jennifer had been put down for the night. It was then that she noticed that Kevin's cheeks were flushed and that his disposition had turned decidedly cranky.

Putting on her most martial demeanour, she got him through the nightly rigmarole of teeth-brushing and pyjamas and tucked-in sheets. He looked tiny and fragile in his large captain's bed with its vivid blue and red spread of Star Wars rocket ships and, when Tamara leaned down to kiss his forehead, she discovered that his skin was burning hot. Thermometer, she thought to herself, and, going into the bathroom, dug through the medicine cabinet until she found one. It wasn't until she actually had the slender glass tube in her hand that she realised she had never used a thermometer before.

'You know how to work this thing, champ?'

'Mommy shakes it first.'

'Right.'

Just for good measure, she shook it from both ends, peered at it intensely and decided that it was reading below normal.

'It goes under my tongue,' Kevin offered helpfully.

'Okay. And how long does it stay there?'

Kevin frowned at her. 'Don't you know, Aunt Tam?'

'Of course, *I* do,' Tamara said stoutly. 'I was just checking to see if *you* did.'

Five minutes later, she was again studying the thermometer. Even to her untrained eye, it was obvious the mercury had risen significantly.

'Aspirin,' she declared crisply, 'some apple juice and a good night's sleep. That's what the doctor ordered.'

'Are you a doctor, Aunt Tam?'

'No, but I once played a nurse in a play called *Blood and Tears*. I'll bet you never heard of that one, champ.'

Kevin shook his head.

'No one else did either. Now, where did Mommy say she kept all the kids' medicines?'

'I only like the orange ones,' he said, his voice trembling a bit. 'I don't want the red, yucky stuff.'

The medications were in a special, locked drawer in the bathroom off the master bedroom and, fortunately, the orange ones were the St Joseph's baby aspirins. Tamara read the instructions and gave Kevin two to chew down along with a glass of apple juice. He fell off to sleep after that, and Tamara decided it would probably be wise if she slept in Guy's and Rebecca's bed since it was near Kevin's bedroom. She knew that if he woke up during the night, she would never hear him from her own room.

The next morning, she dragged herself out of bed when Jennifer began crying. Kevin had been up three times during the night. He had been hot, thirsty, shaky and feverish. He had cried for his parents and, at one point, in the smallest hour of the morning, had seemed inconsolable. She had taken him into bed with her after that, and he had finally fallen asleep after a seemingly interminable time of turning and kicking and making small noises in his throat. Tamara had carried him back to his bed, collapsed into her own and prayed for a few hours of solid sleep. By the time Jennifer woke her up at six o'clock, she felt somewhat akin to the living dead.

It was one of those mornings when nothing seemed to go right. Jennifer didn't want to eat, played with her food and ended up smearing cereal and orange juice all over her face and hair. After she had been cleaned up from that, she gave Tamara a big grin and then dirtied her nappy. Kevin tried to eat some breakfast, vomited the little he had eaten, and cried when

Tamara suggested that he get changed. Rather than fight him, she let him lay on the couch in the family room and watch television. He lay under an old blanket, still in his stained pyjamas and whined periodically. Tamara had forgotten to phone the carpool and cancel Kevin's ride to school. As a result she was forced to make a profuse apology to a pleasant woman who had come a mile out of her way to pick Kevin up. On top of that, she burnt her toast, and her coffee went cold while she changed Jennifer for the umpteenth time. She thought the final straw was knocking over the jug full of orange juice when the doorbell rang, but it wasn't. The thing that really pushed Tamara to the end of her admittedly short tether was the man standing on the front stoop when she threw open the door.

'You,' she accused, her eyes narrowed and supicious. 'What do you want?'

Nothing would have dragged Jake over to the McLaren house when Guy and Rebecca were gone except for the children. He had promised Guy to stop in occasionally to check on them and see how Tamara was doing, but he would have done it anyway. And 'occasionally' didn't suit the way he felt about Guy's kids. He was very fond of Jennifer and Kevin; in fact, he thought he might take the little boy out at the weekend to see the zoo or go for a drive. When he had climbed in the jeep this morning to drive to work, it had occurred to him that Guy's house wasn't so far out of his way that he couldn't stop by every morning just to see how things were going.

He hadn't, of course, expected Tamara to be particularly welcoming or even gracious but, on the other hand, he hadn't expected outright hostility either. Her hair, which was framing her face in a mass of red-orange curls, seemed to be emitting angry sparks, her eyes glinted and her mouth had a curl of derision. Yet, the hardness of her face was at distinct odds with the softness of her body. Jake hadn't actually seen Tamara in weeks so he hadn't witnessed the slow changes brought on by her pregnancy. Her breasts gently lifted the bodice of her long, blue robe and, beneath them, the mound of her abdomen pushed the robe's zipper into a metallic curve. Delicate and slender ankles peeked between the hem of her robe and the tops of her fluffy blue slippers.

Before he had known about her pregnancy, Jake would have answered Tamara in kind, but there was something about a woman in her condition that brought out at least a small vestige of the gentleman in him. 'It's cold out here,' he remarked. 'Can I come in?'

She stepped backwards reluctantly, allowing Jake to enter and close the door behind him. He was pulling off his hat when the cacophony of sounds hit him. There was the television going full tilt, Kevin's whiny voice saying, 'Aunt Tam?' over and over again and then Jennifer's loud wail.

'What's going on here?' he asked and then immediately regretted his tone. It sounded accusing, and he knew it would make Tamara's hackles rise with indignation.

She crossed her arms over her chest. 'Is this an inquisition?' she queried acidly.

Jake raised his hands in a gesture of surrender. 'A friendly visit from the enemy. Just reconnoitring the territory at the request of the absent general. Seriously, Guy asked me to stop by and make sure things were going well.'

Tamara softened a bit. 'Things are going moderately badly. Kevin's sick, Jennifer has no doubt lost her rattle and there's a puddle of orange juice in the middle of the kitchen floor.'

Jake sorted through that and said, 'How sick is Kevin?'

'He's running a fever and he threw up.'

'What does that mean?'

'How should I know?' Tamara yawned in spite of herself. 'I'm not a doctor.'

Jake then noticed the faint circles under her eyes. 'Did Kevin keep you up last night?'

Tamara yawned again. 'He slept with me or —what I should say is—he slept and thrashed and I listened to him breathing.'

Jake was pulling off his coat. 'Let me have a look at him.'

The floor in the kitchen was mopped, Jennifer was restored to her former cheerfulness with a bottle of apple juice and Jake took Kevin upstairs to give him some more aspirin and change him out of his pyjamas. The little boy was happy to see him but definitely hot and cranky. He didn't want to brush his teeth, he objected to having his face washed, and he complained vociferously at getting dressed.

'I don't wanna.'

'Do you want to spend the day in those smelly pyjamas?'

Kevin had a lower lip with a distinctly stubborn pout. 'Yes.'

'Your Mommy and Daddy would want you to get dressed.'

The stubborn lower lip developed a distinct tremor. 'My Mommy isn't here and I want her to come home.'

Oops, Jake thought and hurriedly moved on. 'Hey, listen. Let's make-believe that you're Luke Skywalker and I'm Yoda.'

Kevin looked suspicious.

'And you're after the "power" and I'm going to tell you where it is.'

'Why?'

'Why?' Jake echoed. 'Well, because . . . because Yoda *wants* Luke to find the "power".'

Kevin's big brown eyes were innocent and watchful. 'Why?'

This time Jake's echo was forceful and strong. 'Why? Because he has to get Darth Vader.' Kevin didn't look convinced, but Jake forged ahead anyway. 'So you get your Luke Skywalker shirt on and we'll play.'

Kevin's lower lip started to quiver again. 'I don't have a Luke Skywalker shirt.'

Jake swallowed. 'You don't?'

Kevin shook his head mournfully.

'I thought you got one for Christmas.'

'No.'

Jake stared at the little boy and felt helpless. He

was used to being with Kevin when he was healthy and agreeable; he had never had to deal with a sick child before. He could see that it was going to require tact, patience and ingenuity. He had just started to rack his brains for another subtle means of convincing Kevin that he should get dressed when the little boy spoke again.

'I have a Darth Vader shirt though.'

Jake breathed a sigh of relief. 'Great!' he said. 'You put that on and I'll be Luke Skywalker instead.'

But Kevin blinked at him sadly and shook his head. 'I don't want to be Darth Vader, Uncle Jake. I don't like him.'

An hour later, Jake descended the stairs alone. Kevin was clean, changed and fast asleep, but it had taken every bit of energy that Jake could summon to achieve that end. Kevin had not been co-operative; not even when Jake had been reduced to being a racing car, varooming around the bedroom and making sounds like a V-8 engine. Tamara had peeked in the room at that point and grinned derisively at him, but he had been too tired to care. Now, all he wanted was a chance to sit down and wipe his sweating brow, but there was still the office to look after and the fact that he was going to have to take Kevin to the doctor. He expressed this to Tamara as he pulled on his suit jacket.

'Why?' she asked, looking up from her perusal of a magazine. She was sitting in the kitchen and sipping a glass of milk. She had changed out of her robe into a pair of black slacks and a blue maternity top with a bow at the collar. There was nothing the slightest bit exotic about her at the moment. She wasn't wearing any make-up, and she had the freshly-scrubbed look of a young girl. Freckles ran in a spray along either cheekbone, emphasising their angularity. Her eyelashes and eyebrows were a pale orange, and her hair was pulled away from her face with a band of blue. If Jake hadn't known better; if he hadn't known that she was almost thirty, a woman who had slept around and was now pregnant without even knowing the father of her child, he would have guessed that she was a young housewife, innocent of life and, because of that seeming innocence, almost pretty.

Jake straightened his tie which had become loosened during the Darth Vader stage of his play with Kevin. 'He has spots.'

'Spots?'

'On his chest. Red spots.'

'You mean—like measles?'

Jake shrugged. 'Could be. I'd better take him to the doctor and find out. Can you call and make an appointment some time this afternoon?'

'I'll take him,' she said.

'You don't drive.'

'I'll call a taxi.'

'I said I'd do it,' he insisted.

Tamara put down her glass. 'Is this some sort of macho thing?'

'What do you mean?'

'You know—the cowboy saves the damsel in distress and then rides off into the sunset with the rifle across his saddle while the yellow harvest moon rises over the purple sage of the mesa.'

Jake stared at her. 'I've never ridden a horse in my life. What the hell are you talking about anyway?'

Tamara looked bored. 'I'm talking about your assumption that I am too helpless to take care of Kevin on my own.'

'I didn't say that.'

'You implied it though.'

The old antagonism was rearing its ugly head again. Jake felt the irritation rising within him at her stubbornness, at the placid way she was sitting there and sipping at her milk as if everything were under control and at that faintly amused smile on her face suggesting that what he was offering to her was useless and trivial. Suddenly, she didn't look innocent and almost pretty to him at all. He had been sucked in, he realised, by the tender point of her chin, the clarity of her blue eyes and the swell of her abdomen. The gentleman in Jake was rapidly yielding to his more angry counterpart.

'I only wanted to help,' he ground out through clenched teeth.

'Fine,' she replied airily.

'And you don't want me to.'

'Why should I? I'm perfectly capable of taking Kevin to the doctor.'

'You'll have to take Jennifer, too.'

'It will be an outing for her, and for me.'

'It would be easier if I did it.'

'Look,' Tamara said, leaning forward, her eyes

glinting at him, 'I didn't expect this to be easy. And I'm used to doing things the hard way.'

Jake couldn't help it. The words were out of his mouth before he could stop them. 'Like having a baby without a husband?'

Another woman might have glared at him or replied with angry words but, of course, Tamara didn't fit in any mould. She leaned back in her chair and gave him a knowing smile. 'So,' she nodded, 'the truth will out. You really object to this pregnancy, don't you?'

Jake shifted uncomfortably from his position leaning against the doorjamb. 'I don't think you have the resources to have a baby.'

'I don't.'

'Then you shouldn't have it or you should give it up for adoption.'

Her voice was cool. 'I have the right of choice and I choose to go through with the pregnancy and keep the baby.'

God, how he disliked her. 'You shouldn't have that choice.'

'Are you saying that society should have the right to decide who keeps a child and who doesn't? Do you think some buttoned-down bureaucrat should have the right to decide whether I am old enough or competent enough to bring a child into this world and keep it?'

Jake straightened up and jammed his fists into the pockets of his slacks. 'I'm not going to enter a debate about abstract principles with you. I just have an old-fashioned notion that a child deserves a decent home and two parents.'

'Why?'

He felt like he was strangling. 'What do you mean—why?'

'Why does it have to be like that? What's wrong with some of those other old-fashioned traditions —like making do with what you've got and the gift of love? What's wrong with that?'

The anger burst in him then, the irritation giving way to a tidal wave of fury. He would have liked to take Tamara in his hands and shake the living daylights out of her. He would have liked to throttle her so hard that her head wobbled on its delicate stem and that complacent, knowing look vanished. The urge to do physical violence was so powerful that Jake had to stand rigidly against the wall and forcibly hold himself there.

'You can theorise all you like,' he declared harshly, 'but reality isn't like that at all.'

Her voice was light, mocking. 'No?'

The thought had been there all along, lying below the surface of his consciousness and feeding his seemingly irrational anger. Jake hadn't understood why Tamara's pregnancy made him so furious, but now the reason was pressing on him, forcing him to drag the misery of his past into the present, and shaping it into reluctant words. 'Maybe you won't be able to make do so easily, and maybe that gift of love won't last through your poverty. I grew up with a father who had no money and a mother who left before I can even remember what she looked like. I know what it's like to have a childhood that was hell. You don't.'

That pointed chin lifted a fraction. 'I've had my own personal hells,' she revealed. 'You don't have an exclusive claim to an unhappy childhood.'

'So why inflict one on someone else?'

Colour had found its way into her pale cheeks; two smudges of pink. 'You don't give me much credit, do you? You don't think I can bring up a child responsibly.'

'You didn't have the responsibility of even knowing the father. Why should I assume you'll be able to do anything else?'

Now, she was standing, her hands pressed hard against the table, the swell of her abdomen rising over it. 'What is this—a morality play? Is your glass house so pristine that I can't throw a stone? I've heard all about your girl-friends and how you sleep around.' Her voice was acerbic. 'How many bastards have you fathered?'

Clipped, curt. 'None—I make sure I don't.'

'Well, I was careful too, but even modern medical technology has its flaws. I didn't ask for this child, and it's true that I don't know who fathered it, but at least I want it. At least I know I'll love it.' Her voice lowered to a hiss. 'Maybe you're jealous; maybe your life is so empty of love that you envy me what I have. Maybe that's what's behind your moral posturing and your patronising condescension.'

He hated her; that's how Jake felt, and he hadn't hated too many people in his life. He was an amiable man, usually slow to anger and un-accustomed to the way it could make his insides churn or narrow his vision to the point that he could only focus on that pale face with its freckles and flushed cheeks, its narrow nose and tight-lipped grimace, its burning bush of hair, the tendrils crackling in the sunlight like fire. His hatred was a defence, but Jake didn't realise that. The emotion smothered the truth of her barb and the unerring way she had seen into his soul. It soothed the scar she had opened and the hurt she had inflicted. He only knew that he had to get away before he actually did what his hands itched to do—take her and shake her until she begged and pleaded for mercy.

'I'll come back tomorrow,' he promised coldly, 'to see how Kevin is.'

'You could phone.'

'Damn it!' he swore. 'I'm Kevin's godfather. I have a right to come and see him.'

She shrugged then, that infuriating, careless shrug. 'All right,' she agreed. 'Have it your own way.'

Of course, Tamara ended up regretting what she had done. Kevin cried all the way to the doctor's surgery. He was scared, he said, of needles. Tamara could understand that—she didn't like injections either—but her sympathy didn't have much effect on Kevin who was, despite doses of aspirin and juice, running a constant temperature. And his spots were spreading rapidly. They had started on his chest and back and were now on his legs and upper arms. There were even a few spots on his cheeks, and a couple of the mothers in the waiting-room glanced at him and then moved themselves, and their children, as far away as possible from contamination.

The paediatrician's schedule was running late so Tamara had to deal with a whimpering Kevin and a restless Jennifer who refused to be fascinated by the piles of toys in one corner of the waiting-room. She fussed and fidgeted, wiggled and drooled. She was a demon crawler, too. All Tamara had to do was put her down on the floor and she was off in a second, usually heading towards a light plug or a wire or the door. No matter how many times she was turned around and headed in a different direction, Jennifer obstinately set off again the way she had originally wanted to go. By the time the nurse called Tamara into the office, she was beginning to feel the strain of caring for two unco-operative children. Her head was pounding and her back ached. For the first time the weight of her unborn baby seemed to be pulling her down. It made her wonder what sort of hell it would be when she was nine months pregnant instead of six.

Tamara and the children were in and out of the doctor's surgery in precisely ten minutes. Kevin, it turned out, had a clear-cut case of chicken-pox and was merely another statistic in a minor epidemic that had hit Calgary after Christmas. The doctor prescribed aspirins, lotion and baking soda baths for the itching, and inquired if Tamara had ever had chicken-pox. Since she had vivid memories of being stricken with it, he looked relieved and told her that probably Jennifer

would be next. In seven to ten days, he said. That
was the incubation period. In the mean time,
there was nothing she could do but smile and
cope.

Tamara bundled a protesting Jennifer and a
whiny Kevin back in their snowsuits and took
them home by cab. She gave them a snack and
put them both to bed, hoping that she herself
could get a short rest. Kevin, however, had a
different idea. Since he had spent the morning
sleeping, he was wide awake and wanted to play.
He kept wandering into her bedroom until she
gave up on the idea of sleep and let him build
blocks on her bed. By dinnertime, she was dragging herself around and wondering if it was
kosher to give both children a shot of whisky in
their chicken noodle soup. She put Jennifer in a
Jolly Jumper after dinner in the hopes of tiring her
out, and she let Kevin watch *Charlie's Angels* on
television, a show that Rebecca had ruled as
forbidden because of its violence. Tamara already
admired Rebecca for her serenity and the sweet
way she handled her children, but her admiration
at this point knew no bounds. Rebecca had standards that she adhered to; she, on the other hand,
let the banner droop the moment the going got
tough.

The night was essentially a repeat performance
of the one before it, except that now Kevin, in
addition to running a fever, had started to itch.
He woke frequently and complained loudly. By
the time morning arrived, Tamara estimated that
she had had four hours of sleep in bits and

snatches. It had been a nightmarish mix of child-care and bad dreams. What she remembered of it was seemingly endless trips to the bathroom with Kevin where she daubed lotion on his tiny chest, narrow shoulders and skinny limbs, and equally endless hours when she tossed and turned in bed, either trying to sleep or sleeping so fit-fully she felt as if her eyes hadn't closed all night. When Jennifer's cheerful morning noises sounded down the hall, Tamara pulled herself out of bed and desperately sought to find the energy necessary to deal with a bouncy, healthy and very hungry infant.

She didn't even bother to brush her teeth, comb her hair or put a robe over the nightgown that Rebecca had lent her. It was too long, far too wide and made of white flannel with pink sprigged flowers on it. In order to keep from tripping over the hem, she hitched it up under her breasts and tied the roll of fabric there with a red leather belt that no longer went around her vanished waistline. Because the effort of chang-ing and dressing Jennifer always made her hot, she rolled the sleeves up into huge sloppy cuffs and unbuttoned the Victorian-style lace neckline. And that was the state Jake found her in when he rang the doorbell at eight o'clock that morning, looking flushed and exhausted with her hair in a wild, orange halo around her head, her body swathed in lumpy folds of demure flannel, a smiling baby on her hip, its fat hand pulling the collar of her nightgown out so that he could see the freckled swell of one loose breast.

'Good morning,' he said as he came in.

His forced cheerfulness grated on her, as did his obvious strength and health. It was clear that Jake had spent his night sleeping like the proverbial log. 'What's good about it?' she replied.

He hung his suede coat in the foyer closet, pulled off his fur hat and turned to her. 'You look like hell,' he commented in a matter-of-fact voice.

Tamara gave him a sour look and loosened Jennifer's hold on her nightgown. 'Thanks.'

'Kevin kept you up last night?'

'Kevin has the beginnings of a virulent case of chicken-pox.'

'Is he up?'

'He's asleep.'

'What about you?'

Tamara gave him a look of surprise. 'Me? What about me?'

'Why don't you try to get some sleep?'

'And what should I do with Jennifer?' she asked acidly. 'Let her roam around the house on her own?'

'I'll take care of her.'

'Don't you have to go to the office?'

'It's slow right now; that's why Guy took a vacation.'

Tamara stared at him, saw that his offer of help was sincere, and felt the seductive pull of her bed. She *was* exhausted; she *did* look like hell. And she knew precisely how the rest of the day would go. By the time Kevin woke up, bright-eyed and bushy-tailed, Jennifer would be ready for a nap, and when Jennifer was up and alert in the late afternoon, Kevin would need a sleep before dinner. And so it would go all day with Tamara rushing from child to child, never once getting a chance to sleep herself. Add another disturbed night on top of that, and there was a good chance she would be ready for a loony-bin by the next morning.

'I didn't do last night's dishes,' she warned.

'I'll clean up.'

'There are toys all over the family room.'

'No sweat.'

'And Jennifer needs her nappy changed.'

Jake reached for the baby, and she gurgled at him and stretched her arms in his direction. 'We get along like a house on fire, don't we, Jen?' Jake murmured to her as Tamara handed her over to him.

'Da-da,' Jennifer said and Jake beamed.

'Have you ever changed a nappy?' Tamara asked suspiciously.

'Have I ever changed a nappy?' Jake grinned and held a delighted Jennifer up in the air so that she drooled on his tie. 'Jennifer, have I ever changed a nappy? Of course, I have. I'm a fast hand with a nappy-pin and I even know the jargon. Fold in front for a boy; fold behind for a girl.'

'Jennifer wears Pampers,' Tamara returned coldly, 'and they have adhesive tapes.'

'Every day I bow down to the god of modern technology and give him thanks for his munificence. Hit the sack, Tamara, you look like you need it.'

Grudgingly, Tamara headed towards the stairs. 'And don't forget to put the Denison cream on her. She's got a bit of nappy rash. And the lotion for Kevin is in the master bed bathroom and, if he gets too itchy, you can always stick him in a bath. He should have an aspirin when he wakes up and . . .'

'Sweet dreams, Tamara,' smiled Jake with a touch of sarcasm.

She turned slightly to glance at him before she started up the stairs, and this was the image that she carried to her bed with her: Jake holding Jennifer in his arms, his head bent as he kissed the roundness of her cheek, his thick wheat-coloured hair brushing Jennifer's white-blonde curls. The baby was reaching down to grab his tie, and one of her fat, bare feet had wiggled its way into the lapel of his finely cut grey jacket. Because their colouring was so similar, they looked like father and daughter and, because Jake was so big and Jennifer was so small, the image held an aura of sweet vulnerability and male protectiveness.

Tamara felt a lump rise in her throat and tears prick behind her eyes. She hurried up the stairs, cursing herself for a sentimental fool. She never cried, nothing had ever made her cry. Not her father's betrayal, her mother's anger, running away from home, or her own failures and mistakes. She was made of tougher stuff than that, and she attributed the maudlin attack to her pregnancy. It was making her susceptible to the most cliché'd scenes; to the sight of a grown man and a baby, to a kiss on a round, innocent cheek, to fat toes against grey herringbone.

In the past, Tamara wouldn't have given a damn about stuff like that. She would have shrugged it off, mocked it and then ignored it. That was the kind of attitude that had got her through hell and back, and she didn't intend to lose it simply because her hormone level was in flux. She couldn't afford to let the tough part of herself soften or yield. Life was going to be hard for her; she knew that. It always had been and it always would be. If there was one thing that Tamara had learned from early childhood on, it was that the world not only didn't owe her a living, it didn't give hand-outs of happiness either. She had had to struggle for every good moment, for every smile, for every laugh she had ever laughed. That was one of the reasons she didn't laugh too often. The fight had been too hard; the battle so wearying that merely coming through unbroken had been enough.

CHAPTER SEVEN

WHEN Tamara awoke three hours later she showered and dressed, changing into her blue and purple caftan with the gold threads worked in the neckline and hem, pulling the purple headband around her forehead to hold down the springy mass of her hair and attaching a pair of large gold hoops to her ears. The rest of the house was quiet when she went down the stairs, and she found Jennifer playing in her high chair with a set of keys, Kevin neat, except for the daubs of lotion on his face, watching television and Jake preparing a lunch of cream of mushroom soup and tuna fish sandwiches. The house had been picked up, straightened and cleaned, and he looked exceedingly domestic with his jacket and tie off, a large pink floral apron wrapped around his waist, standing in front of the sink and rinsing out a mixing bowl.

He glanced at her as she came in. 'Rested?' he asked.

'Yes, thanks.'

'Would you like a cup of coffee?'

'Actually, I'd prefer a glass of milk.'

'Right.' He served her a tall glass of milk and then joined her at the table. 'Look, I've been thinking about this, and there's no reason why you have to bear the problem of Kevin's chicken-pox alone.'

'I . . .'

'No, hear me out. I still have to go to work during the day, but I can come and stay here at night and help you with the children.' His voice was careful as if he were treading across a piece of land booby-trapped with mines. 'I'm not trying to say that you can't care for them, I know you're perfectly capable of coping on your own, but it's a hard thing to do when you can't get enough sleep. At the rate you're going you'll be sicker than Kevin is. You need your sleep; remember, you're sleeping for two.'

Tamara opened her mouth and then shut it again. Of course, he was right, and everything he had said was reasonable. Her coping mechanisms would break down if she didn't get more sleep at night, and the pregnancy was draining her of her normal energy level. It made a lot of sense to have two adults in the house instead of one who was operating at semi-efficiency. And the fact that she and Jake detested one another shouldn't stand in the way of caring for the children. They deserved the best, and she knew she couldn't give it to them if she had to be up with Kevin half the night.

'I guess that's a good idea,' she nodded.

Jake looked relieved, and she realised that he had expected a rejection from her and probably an angry tirade into the bargain. 'I'll go home from the office today and pick up some clothes. I should be here in time for dinner.'

'I hope you like hot dogs.'

'Love 'em.'

'And baked beans.'

'My favourite.'

God, Tamara thought, he isn't kidding around
—he does like them. And suddenly she couldn't
stand the hearty smile and this false attempt to be
friendly. 'I just want you to know something,'
she stated coldly. 'I appreciate your offer of help,
and I'm taking you up on it, but as far as I'm
concerned, I still don't like you.'

He leaned back in his chair and appraised her,
his dark eyes glancing from the purple headband
to the swinging gold hoops to the exotic, metallic
pattern of her caftan. 'You're a sweet little thing,
aren't you?'

'I just want to keep it clean.'

'Have no fear. I don't like you either and
haven't since the moment I laid eyes on you.'

'Good.' She stood up. 'Then that's settled.'

'Yup.' Jake stood up as well and stretched so
that she got a full and virile view of powerful
chest muscles straining against the fabric of his
white shirt. 'That's settled.'

The Calgary winter set in with a vengeance after
that, and Tamara couldn't help being thankful for
Jake's presence. The mercury dropped to 40
below with a wind chill factor of −72 degrees.
The sun was a smoky yellow disc in an intense
blue sky, and the air was so dry that Tamara's hair
crackled when she brushed it. Outside, the wind
blew constantly, the howl of its voice roaring

around the corners of the house, groaning down the chimney and whispering in every nook and cranny it could find. Jake went around caulking leaks and fixing weather-stripping. When a shutter came off and banged against the side of the house with a deafening regularity, he dressed himself in down-filled trousers and a jacket and spent fifteen minutes up on a ladder, putting it back into place. The silence was blessed after that, and Tamara, in a gesture of thanks, handed him a hot rum toddy when he came in, his fingers half-frozen and his eyelashes encrusted with ice.

And he ran the errands that would have been so hard for Tamara to do. He stopped at the drugstore for more children's aspirin and lotion. He visited a toy store and came back with an armful of extra colouring books and toys since Rebecca's supply had only lasted three days. Realising the monotony of frozen hamburgers and canned foods, he brought a pizza back one night and Chinese food two days later. He also visited the library for Tamara, rented a movie for the video and stopped at the only store in Calgary that carried foreign papers and magazines. For the first time in months, Tamara was able to delve through the gossip column in *Variety* and read the theatre reviews in the *New York Times*. Not that it seemed to matter so much any more. The world of Broadway felt far away to her now as if she were on another planet, in another universe. Sheila had written to her a couple of times, but neither of them were great correspondents, and she had only heard from Martine once, a

Christmas card which arrived two weeks
after New Year. As far as Tamara was concerned,
New York hardly existed at all.

There was also no doubt that Jake was wonderful with the children. He kept Kevin amused
which was a job unto itself. He had a seemingly
inexhaustible supply of patience for intricate
block-building projects and Corgi car races. He
liked to read aloud and didn't seem to mind that
Kevin wanted to hear the *Green Eggs and Ham* for
the twentieth time. He even put expression into
it, making Tamara smile reluctantly to herself
when she overheard him. 'I would not, could not,
in a box,' he would say with a highly dramatic
intonation. 'I could not, would not, with a fox.'
He was even willing to sit with Kevin during the
long, baking soda bath sessions which they
found was the best way to keep the itching down
to a bearable minimum.

Tamara didn't know what she would have
done without Jake as Kevin's spots increased,
grew larger, and crusted over. The doctor had
told her that if he scratched off the crusts, scars
would remain. They were able to talk Kevin into
wearing gloves some of the time, but it was an
all-consuming job to keep him under constant
surveillance. And he still got up several times
during the night. To Tamara's relief, Jake insisted
on taking over the nocturnal guard duty; she
knew she couldn't have stood one more day
without a solid eight hours of sleep. She moved
out of the master bedroom and back into her own
bed, leaving Jake with the burden of Kevin's

wakefulness. The lack of sleep didn't seem to bother him all that much. Except for a few extra wrinkles around the eyes, he looked as fresh as a daisy every morning.

In fact, if it weren't for the mutual animosity underlying their polite words and gestures and the way they skirted around one another to avoid conflict, Tamara and Jake essentially got along very well. They divided up the work in equal parts; both cooked, both cleaned up and both of them took care of the children. When they were forced to be together, they talked about safe and non-controversial topics such as the Canadian political situation, the erratic Calgary weather, the state of oil and gas exploration and new office development downtown. Fortunately, however, the house was big enough so that they weren't on top of one another all the time, and this certainly helped their undeclared moratorium of peace.

In the evenings Tamara would usually go to her room and read. She had never had time to read anything except plays before, and she now threw herself into the world of romances, mysteries and thrillers. The only non-fiction she read were books on pregnancy, and these she had almost memorised. She didn't know what Jake did when she closeted herself in her room, but he seemed to keep himself amused. She suspected that he did office work, because at the end of the day, he always brought home a briefcase crammed full with papers. Since she had no interest in him, she never asked.

But there was one area of their co-existence in

which perfect peace and harmony reigned and their antagonism was forgotten. When it came to the children, Tamara and Jake were in absolute accord. In fact, their spirit of co-operation was so great that, during the first real crisis of Kevin's illness, not only did they act in unison, but they hadn't even needed words to co-ordinate their effort. They had been able to read one another's intent by glances, shrugs and smiles.

'Oh, my God,' Tamara said with foreboding. 'I forgot to tell you—Rebecca's going to phone tonight.'

They were in the living room with the children after dinner. She was folding a pile of laundry and Jake was lying on his back before the fireplace with Jennifer trying to crawl up his chest and Kevin making loud, car noises beside his ear. 'What?'

'Rebecca said she'd phone on Tuesday night. She's going to want to talk to Kevin.'

That made Jake sit up, his large hand tucked under Jennifer's small, nappy-covered bottom so that she wouldn't fall over. He put her down on the floor beside him where she picked up a doll and started to chew on its fingers. Jake took a deep breath, brushed his fingers through the tousled strands of his hair and gave Tamara a look that let her know they were thinking along the same, worried lines.

'Damn,' he said and Kevin stopped playing with his cars.

'That's a bad word, Uncle Jake,' he scolded.

'Kevin, my boy, you're smart, you know that?

So smart that we're going to make up a little game.'

Kevin loved games. 'What game?'

Jake glanced at Tamara and she nodded. 'It's called "talking to Mommy in Mexico." Aunt Tam will be Mommy, and we'll use the play phone. Okay?'

Kevin couldn't help looking bewildered. 'That doesn't sound like a game.'

'It is, Kevin, and it's fun.'

Tamara joined them on the floor and, miming a telephone conversation, put an invisible receiver up to her ear. 'Ring, ring,' she jangled.

Jake handed Kevin the pink play phone. 'Answer it,' he told him. 'Maybe it's Mommy.'

Kevin looked at both adults as if they were slightly wacky, but he was, by nature, an obedient little boy. He put the receiver of the play phone up to his ear. 'Hello?' he asked tentatively.

Tamara smiled and injected Rebecca's bright enthusiasm into her voice. 'Hi, Kevin. It's Mommy.'

'Hi, Mommy.'

'Are you being a good boy?'

'Uh-uh.'

'Are you listening to Aunt Tam?'

'Yes.'

'And being good to Jennifer?'

'Yes.'

'And how's school?'

'I'm not going to school, Mommy. I've got chicken-pox.'

Jake quickly intervened. 'This is a special game,

Kevin, and the important part is that Mommy isn't supposed to know that you have chicken-pox.'

Kevin looked uncertainly from Jake to Tamara and then back. 'She isn't?'

'No, we don't want Mommy to worry about you. That would ruin her holiday. She might think she has to come home.'

'But I'd like Mommy to come home.'

Jake threw Tamara a panicky look and she stepped in. 'Kevin, honey, you know that Mommy loves you and she'll worry if she knows you have chicken-pox. You wouldn't want her to worry when you have Uncle Jake and me to take care of you, would you?'

Kevin's dark eyes were big in his spotted, little face. 'I guess not.'

Jake pulled him up on his lap, gave him a big hug and threw a grin in Tamara's direction. 'Good boy,' he said. 'Let's play it again.'

The sunset had turned the sky over the rolling waters of the Pacific a magnificent and glowing shade of purple, and the few clouds lining the horizon like cotton batting ranged in colour from pink to orange. With dusk the air had cooled slightly, but the Mexican night was still warm and balmy. Rebecca came in from the balcony off their hotel room and closed the sliding screen door behind her. 'It's so lovely,' she breathed. 'Why do we live in Calgary?'

'Because I earn a living there,' Guy explained gently, coming up to her and pulling her into his arms. He had just come out of a shower and was naked except for a white towel around his middle. His hair was still wet and made dark curls around his forehead and ears. 'You wouldn't want to live here anyway. The Mexican economy is in a terrible condition.' He nuzzled her neck, folding away the collar of her sundress. 'Mmmm—you smell like ocean and sun—my favourite combination.'

'Oh, no,' she scolded, pushing him away slightly. 'I've got to call home. I said I would.'

His dark eyes gleamed down at her. 'How about later?' he asked. 'Right now, I'd like to commit an intimate act with you.'

Rebecca smiled up at him and wound her arms around his neck, enjoying the feel of his bare skin under her fingers. Guy had been right; the vacation was worth the time, the effort and the money. She had quite forgotten what it was like to be alone with her husband with nothing to do but lounge in the sun, enjoy someone else's cooking and make love at any hour of the day that they pleased. She brushed her lips against his and said, 'If I call later, Kevin will be asleep.'

He kissed her back. 'That's true.'

'And, admit it, I've been very good. I haven't spent hours worrying about them.'

'I've been keeping you too busy to do that.'

'Mmmm—I've noticed.'

He gave her a kiss then that was long and deep and very satisfactory. She pushed him away after it, gave him a swift pat on his terry-towellinged rear and said, 'So how about we commit an intimate and perverted act after the phone call?'

'Perverted? Now, that sounds interesting. What do you plan to do?'

'Half the fun,' she teased, 'is in the surprise.'

It took a while to make the telephone connection, and the line between Canada and Mexico crackled like bacon in a frying pan, but Rebecca found herself smiling when she heard the ringing and could imagine the white phone against the patterned paper on her kitchen wall. But when the phone was answered, it was a male voice that spoke and she blinked with surprise.

'Hello?' she queried hesitantly.

'Rebecca? It's Jake.'

She turned towards Guy who was lying on the bed next to her. 'It's Jake!' she told him and then talked into the receiver. 'What are you doing there?'

'Just checking up.'

'Is everything okay.'

'It's great and . . .'

His voice faded away. 'Jake! I can't hear you.'

'. . . is terrific and the kids are just fine. Would you like to talk to Kevin?'

'Please.'

'Kevin's treble was faint. 'Mommy?'

'Hi, darling.' Rebecca could just see him in her mind's eye, pressing the telephone tightly to his ear, his eyes wide with anxiety. Kevin was still young enough to be nervous about talking on the telephone. 'Are you being a good boy?'

'Yes.'

'And you're helping Aunt Tam with Jennifer?'

'Yes.'

'And you're going to bed when you're supposed to?'

'Yes.'

'And what about school, Kevin? Are you being a good boy there?' Suddenly there was a silence. 'Kevin?' Then garbled voices and finally Kevin was back on. Rebecca thought he sounded a bit breathless, but it could have been the connection.

'Fine, Mommy.'

'That's good, darling. Would you like to talk to Daddy?'

'Yes.'

Guy had an equally cryptic conversation with Kevin, then he spoke briefly to Jake and, when Tamara was on the line, handed the phone back to Rebecca.

'How are the *enchiladas*?' Tamara asked.

'Delicious. It sounds as if you've got everything under control.'

'No problems here. We're as snug as bugs in a rug.'

'Has Jake been coming by often?'

'Uh—not often.' There was a pause that was distinctly uncomfortable. 'No, I wouldn't put it that way.'

'He really is very good with the children, isn't he?'

'Marvellous.'

'Well, I'm glad to hear everything's fine.'

'Don't worry about us. Have a good time. Are you learning any Spanish?'

'A little.'

'*Adios* then.'

'I'll call next week. Bye.'

Rebecca put down the phone and gave Guy a tremulous smile. 'I guess they didn't miss us at all.'

'See—I told you.'

'Isn't it odd that Jake was there. I wouldn't have thought . . . well, maybe he and Tam are getting along a little better than they used to.' She paused a bit and stared out of the screened door to the horizon which had now darkened to a deep royal blue, the lowering sun a wide golden curve against the black of the sea. 'Maybe there still is a chance that the two of them will . . .'

'Oh, no, you don't.' Guy was firm. 'I don't want you to be interested in anyone else's sex life.' He put his hand on his abdomen where one edge of the towel was tucked into the other. 'You promised, remember?'

Rebecca put her hand over his and smiled. 'I remember,' she said.

Kevin's chicken-pox slowly abated, the fever disappearing and the spots vanishing as if they had never existed. Thanks to Jake's and Tamara's care and intervention, Kevin hadn't scratched hard enough to do himself permanent and visible damage. The one scar he had left was on the back of his left knee. Tamara saw it, sighed with relief and suggested to Jake that, if it weren't for the necessity of keeping medical records on childhood diseases like chicken-pox, there was really a possibility that Rebecca need never know that her son had once looked like he had been infected with a galloping case of the crud.

By the following Sunday, Kevin was his normal self once again, and Tamara was about to suggest that Jake needn't stay at the house any longer, when they noticed that Jennifer had a few spots on her chest. She didn't eat well, she was the slightest bit cranky, but she didn't run a fever and, by Tuesday, it was evident that Jennifer's brush with chicken-pox was going to be a mild one. Kevin was back in school and life had taken on a regular routine. Jake was coming back to the house that night for dinner, and Tamara decided that she would tell him it was time to go. He hadn't mentioned moving back to his apartment himself, and she would have been blind not to notice that he enjoyed the domesticity of the McLaren household, but she really didn't want Jake around any more. Once they didn't have the children's crises to discuss, she suspected that they would be back at one another's throats.

But he barely ate any dinner that night, he looked sort of grey under the golden shadow of his beard and, when he mentioned having a headache, Tamara gave him a sharp glance.

'What kind of a headache?'

'Dull and achy.'

By now, she was a wizard with a thermometer. She sat Jake on the couch in the living room, shook it expertly down and made him put it under his tongue. 'Five minutes,' she ordered, 'and no talking.'

'Aye, aye, sir,' he mumbled.

'I said—no talking. Kevin, keep an eye on him.'

Kevin's eyes lit up. 'Okay, Aunt Tam.'

When she had got Jennifer changed and into bed, she came down the stairs to find Kevin keeping a watch over a sleeping Jake. The thermometer was on the coffee-table and, picking it up, she brought it over to the light. 'God,' she breathed, staring at the mercury and then down at Jake. He was out cold, his long length taking up all four cushions of the couch, one large hand splayed across the opened front of his suit jacket, the other hanging down almost to the floor. He was sweating slightly and his blond hair was damp over his ears and on his forehead. His face was too broad and his chin too square for him to be classically handsome but, in repose, he had a vulnerable look that was immensely appealing. Tamara tore her eyes away from him and back to the thermometer which, according to the mercury, had registered his temperature at 103 degrees.

'What's the matter, Aunt Tam?'

'I have the awful feeling that Uncle Jake is coming down with chicken-pox, champ.'

'I thought only kids got chicken-pox.'

'So,' she agreed grimly, 'did I.'

There was nothing, Tamara decided over the next few days, more pitiful than a grown man laid low by a disease as humiliating as chicken-pox. Jennifer virtually romped through her bout, Kevin had suffered, but Jake was in absolute misery. He ran a high fever for several days and, when the spots arrived, it appeared that they were on a rampage. The territory they covered was vast, personal and embarrassing. Except for his face, the palms of his hands and the soles of his feet, every square inch of Jake had its share of chicken-pox. Tamara took a taxi to a nearby grocery store to stock up on boxes of baking soda and to a drugstore where she bought jars of aspirin, bottles of lotion and several packages of cotton balls. She became adept at making trays of enticing tid-bits of food to whet his meagre appetite and, when his sheets were soaked with sweat every day, she learned how to change a bed in record time.

He wasn't a bad patient; he slept a lot and he didn't complain. And he was truly grateful for everything Tamara did for him. He apologised frequently and gave her smiles of such breath-taking sweetness, it almost took her breath away. He worried that she would get tired, that she couldn't manage to care for him and the children together, that she would exhaust herself to the point of endangering her pregnancy.

'Don't be silly,' she argued.

He was in her old room, lying naked on his stomach on the bed, a sheet covering him to the waist. Tamara was sitting on the edge of the bed and daubing lotion on him with cotton balls. His back had got the worst of it; he was covered from his scalp down to the backs of his knees. The doctor had prescribed other medication for him, but nothing stopped the itching as well as a baking soda bath followed by a thick coating of lotion.

'All those stairs, the trays, the washing . . .'

'You're disturbing my lotion-applying technique.'

'You're good at it, are you?'

'The best.'

There was silence as she worked her way down from the back of his neck to the spread of his shoulders. He was a man with a fair amount of body hair and each dab of lotion turned the golden hairs a dark shade of pink. Tamara could see that, without the pox marks, Jake would have a very attractive back. It was broad and muscular, tapering down to a narrow waist. She could feel the muscles under his skin bunching, tightening and then relaxing as she touched him.

'I wish my father had kept medical records,' he sighed mournfully.

'That wouldn't have changed anything. You were still exposed to Kevin before we knew it was chicken-pox.'

'I think I had measles once.'

'Did you have mumps?'

'I think so.'

'That's the one that makes grown men sterile if they get it.'

'I'll get down on my hands and knees,' Jake said, turning his face from one side to the other so that his voice was muffled by the pillow, 'and thank the good Lord that he sent me chicken-pox instead of mumps.'

Tamara was now below his shoulder-blades

and working her way down the bumpy path of his spine. 'Are you planning to get married and have children?' she asked.

'No.'

'Why? You like kids.'

'Other people's.'

'That surprises me. I would have thought you'd want some of your own.'

'I'm not a family man.'

'What does that mean?'

He was silent for a moment and then he said, 'I can't see myself in a family situation. I wasn't brought up in one; I don't know how a family works.'

'You've spent enough time with Guy and Rebecca. They have a good marriage. In fact, they're perfect role models.'

'Dropping in on a marriage is different from having one. No, I've never thought I'd be any good at it.'

'Because of your mother leaving?'

'And my father. He was a drunk.'

'Was that why she left? Because he drank?'

'No, he started drinking after that.'

There was something about the way Jake spoke that told Tamara she had started to tread on thin emotional ice, and she quickly changed the subject. 'Our family was the reverse,' she revealed. 'My father was the one who left.'

'How old were you when that happened?'

'About eleven. He and my mother had been fighting for so long that it was inevitable, I suppose. It got so bad that they stopped talking to one another, and Rebecca and I carried messages back and forth for them.'

'What did your father do?'

'He was a salesman for IBM. Upstate New York and New England was his territory. He wasn't home a lot, actually, now that I think about it, but when he was, it was hell around our house.'

'You sound bitter about him.'

Her voice was low. 'I am.'

'Do you still see him?'

'No, he dropped out of our lives like a stone disappearing into water. I know he sent my mother support money for a while, but I don't know how long it lasted. He never . . . cared enough to come back and see us.'

'Daughters are often very attached to their fathers, you know.'

Tamara's hand stopped moving. 'Why do you say that?' she asked sharply.

The big shoulders shrugged. 'Something in your voice suggests that you're bitter because you were close to him.'

'Rebecca wasn't close to him, and . . . Celia was only three.'

'And what about you?'

Tamara's own emotional thin ice trembled as he trod close and, once again, she changed the subject. 'I've reached your waistline,' she told him, shaking the bottle of lotion.

'Oh, hell, do the rest, will you? I'm not shy, and I can hardly sit down. Besides, I'm sure the sight won't be new to you.'

Tamara moved slightly down the edge of the

bed and pulled the sheet along with her, baring Jake's buttocks and thighs. The tautness of his waist led to a tight curve of muscle and legs that were covered with crisp, gold hairs. Backs were backs, but a man's rear was an erogenous zone. Despite the fact that his skin was raw with chicken-pox, Tamara felt a stirring deep within her and, shocked that she could feel even the slightest sexual interest in Jake, tried to suffocate the sensation with an outpouring of pity.

She tched-tched, shook her head and said, 'Poor Jake.'

'What a come-down.' He gave a sigh of depression. 'That isn't what the last woman said.'

Tamara put a cotton ball to the mouth of the bottle and let it absorb the lotion. 'No? What did she say?'

'She said—terrific bum.'

Tamara began dotting his rear with pink daubs. 'Vanity, vanity,' she chided.

'I take it all back, you know,' Jake declared.

'What?'

'The nasty things I said about you.'

'God,' Tamara exclaimed. 'Put a man face down on a bed, expose his ass to the elements and he has revelations.'

'I'm serious,' he pressed on. 'I was wrong to say that you weren't responsible enough to have a child. You were great with the kids and you've been wonderful to me. You may not have any money and the kid may not have a father, but you'll make a fine mother.'

The praise was so unexpected and said so sincerely that Tamara felt tears prick behind her eyes. She forced them back, cleared her throat and said in a tart voice, 'I'll never forget that time I got to play Florence Nightingale. It was carry the bedpans and wipe the sweat off the brows of suffering soldiers. It was forbearance and nobility, heartbreak and silent sorrow. The audience loved the play; the critics thought it was a lot of sentimental slosh pouring out over the orchestra pit and flowing up the aisles.'

'Tamara?'

'Yes?'

Jake's voice was gentle. 'It's all right,' he said, 'to accept my compliments.'

She blinked; the tears were rising again. 'No, it isn't,' she replied quickly.

'Why not?'

'They're meaningless and non-functional.'

'And out of the context of our relationship.'

Her voice was curt. 'Yes.'

'We don't have to fight all the time,' he remarked softly. 'In fact, we've been getting along very well, all things considered.'

'If you didn't have chicken-pox . . .'

'I know—you'd have thrown me out of the house days ago. I've decided something about you, Tamara, and that is—you're not happy unless you're fighting with someone or something. If life's too placid, you get restless and combative. You only know you're alive when you're up against an enemy or fate.'

Considering the way she had held Jake at arm's

length and shielded herself from his scrutiny, it was an oddly perceptive remark. Tamara had never thought about herself in such terms, but Jake had pointed out a pattern of behaviour that had been hers since the time she was a child. She was a struggler, a scrapper, a fighter. She liked nothing better than an uphill battle and an adversary who whetted the sharp edge of her sarcastic tongue. She liked to wage wars; against specific persons, against the world in general, against a fickle and capricious fate. Why else had she kept the battle between Martine and herself going for so long? Why else had she kept on struggling against indifferent directors and a disinterested public? Without a wall to butt her head up against, Tamara wouldn't have known what to do with herself.

'I still don't like you,' she said in a low, stubborn voice.

There was a hint of laughter in his words. 'Is that why you've spent half an hour stroking my bum?'

Tamara lifted her hand as if she had been burnt. The shape of his muscles had been so pleasing that she had quite overdone the application of medication on Jake's rear. It was caked with pink lotion. 'I forgot what I was doing.' She hadn't blushed for years, but now she could feel the heat rise in her cheeks and colour them a bright red.

Jake made a choking sound into the pillow. 'Sure.'

With an efficient snap of her wrists, Tamara

flicked the sheet back up over the portion of his anatomy under discussion and covered her embarrassment with a nurse-like proficiency. 'There you are,' she replied tartly. 'And I suggest you lie still for a while.'

Jake turned over and gave her a grin. 'Did you ever play Florence Nightingale?'

'Would I lie? Would I . . . ?'

'Come on, tell the truth.'

'No,' she confessed reluctantly.

Jake's grin widened with delight. 'That's what I thought.'

Jake didn't know precisely when the change had taken place. It was hard to pin-point the moment when his feeling for Tamara had undergone a subtle transformation from dislike to an absence of dislike, then to liking and now to an active interest. He had, of course, felt an extreme gratitude for all the things she had done for him. Jake wasn't used to being sick; he rarely ever had a cold. In all his life, he had never imagined that it was possible to feel so wretched. The world had seemed hazy when he had had a fever, and his bones had ached with such intensity he hadn't been able to lie in one position for any length of time. He had been so cold that Tamara hadn't been able to pile enough blankets on him, and then so hot, he had wanted drink after drink. Then he had sweated so badly that his sheets had been drenched several times a day.

Tamara had waited on him, hand and foot, and he had come to long for the touch of her fingers, warm when he had been cold and cool when he had been hot. And, without her, the itching of the chicken-pox would have driven him into a frenzy. Without complaint, she had drawn bath after bath for him and willingly applied lotion to him when he was dry. She had done this several times during the day and a couple of times at night when the fever and aching and itching had woken him up. She had smiled at him, talked to him sweetly and treated him with such a dose of sympathetic care that Jake didn't think he would ever want to give it up. He liked to watch her move about the bedroom, straightening the sheets and blankets, fluffing up a pillow, handing him a glass of orange juice.

And he liked the fact that the sweetness was only a part of her personality. It would have been cloying if the contrast with the rest of her hadn't made it so delightful. Jake discovered that he liked the tart side of Tamara as well as the sweet. She wasn't like other women he had known who flirted and covered up their emotions with seductive looks. She didn't mince words, she lied when it suited her purpose, but she could also be honest to the point of inflicting pain. He never quite knew what Tamara would say next, and that was unusual, refreshing and provoking. Jake hadn't known how much he liked being provoked until Tamara had come along to intrigue him.

And her looks and clothes no longer irritated him. Tamara was like an exotic flower, and Jake, who had always subscribed to the classical in

beauty, now discovered that freckles, a sharp-
pointed chin, wide-spaced blue eyes and hair the
colour of boiled carrots had a pleasing air about
them. And, oddly enough, her pregnancy didn't
deter him from finding her desirable. That
shocked him. Like many men, Jake had always
been attracted to women who were slender and
curvaceous. He liked a body that was filled out in
the right places and slender where it counted.
He would have never thought, not in a million
years, that he would find anything sensuous in
a woman whose waistline exceeded her bustline.
He had always thought of pregnant women
as asexual beings, but now he was discovering
that a woman, swollen and bearing another
man's child, was still essentially very feminine.
There was a softness about Tamara that had an
incredible sexual appeal for him.

Jake fought that. He had been celibate for
almost three weeks, and he attributed his lustful-
ness to that distressful state. As his chicken-pox
wore off, he thought about going back to work
and finding a woman again. He ranged through
his latest assortments of blondes and brunettes,
discarding this one and then that one, until he
had gone through the entire list and discovered
that there wasn't one he would want to see again.
They all struck him as boring; he could imagine
what an evening with any of them would be like.
The game was always the same. There was the
flirtation, the knowing smiles and the roll in the
hay. Once, he had enjoyed the inevitability of it
and the confidence that he had in his own

success. Now, the thrill of it had palled. For the first time in his life, Jake was willing to approach a woman whose responses were neither ordinary nor predictable. Of course, he didn't think of Tamara in those terms; he only knew that his interest was piqued and his sexual curiosity aroused. After much deliberation and discomfort, Jake realised that there was only one solution to his problem and, being Jake, decided to act on it.

CHAPTER EIGHT

'Hi, Mommy. Are you and Daddy having a good time?'

Since the connection was so bad, Rebecca held the phone closer to her ear. 'Yes, we are, honey. The sun shines every day and it's very warm. Isn't that nice?'

'Yes.'

'How was school today?'

'Fine.'

'Have you finished dinner?'

'Yes. I was playing cars with Uncle Jake.'

'With Uncle Jake?'

'He was playing ambulance.'

'Does Uncle Jake stop by every night, Kevin?'

'Oh, no, Mommy, he lives here now.'

Pregnant pause. 'He does?'

'Uh-uh, he sleeps in . . .'

'Kevin? Kevin?'

'Hi, Rebecca?'

'Tam, what's going on there?'

'Here? Nothing.'

'Kevin said that Jake was sleeping over there.'

Tamara's laugh was musical and highly amused. 'Heavens, Becks, he's just a little confused.'

'Confused by what?'

'The comings and goings. Jake had to fix one of

the shutters. You should have heard it banging around in the wind, knocking against the house and . . .'

'Tam, I get the distinct feeling that you're not telling me the truth.'

'The truth?'

'The honest-to-god truth.'

'Enjoy the sunshine, Becks, and don't worry about us. *Adios.*'

'Tamara, I . . .' But the connection had been severed, and Rebecca stared suspiciously down at the telephone receiver as if it could tell her more than she had heard. 'Guy, there's something funny going on.'

He was shaving for dinner. 'What?'

'Kevin says that Jake has moved into the house.'

'Kevin has been known to get his facts confused. He is only five.'

Rebecca leaned against the bathroom door and stared moodily at Guy whose chin was covered with lather. 'Where there's smoke, there's fire.'

'Meaning what?'

'Meaning that something's happened between Tamara and Jake. I feel it in my bones.'

He grinned at her. 'Love 'dem bones.'

'Guy, I'm serious. You don't suppose that . . . they're sleeping together, do you? After the way they hated each other? And with Tamara almost seven months pregnant?'

'I refuse to speculate on Jake's and Tamara's amorous habits.'

It was infuriating the way he so calmly ran the

razor down his cheek and over his chin. 'You know, I always said they'd be a perfect match. Jake might not know it but he really wants a woman who sparks his imagination instead of just . . . just . . .'

'Sparking his libido.'

'And Tamara is so intense, she needs someone like Jake. He's easy-going, restful, peaceful.'

Guy glanced at her in the mirror and gave her a mocking look. '"*Matchmaker, matchmaker, make me a match*," ' he sang.

'You have no imagination,' she replied scoldingly.

'Sure I do. I just don't apply it to other people.'

'And I suppose you're going to tell me I'm nosy.'

Guy sprayed some lather on his fingers and, leaning forward, placed a large, white blob of it on her nose and grinned. 'Took the words right out of my mouth.'

Tamara was never quite sure why she let it happen. Certainly, if she had been more prepared, more aware of what was coming, she would have been able to stop, but it was so unexpected, so out-of-the-blue and so surprising that she had simply yielded. And that was astonishing in itself. Tamara rarely acted on that sort of an impulse; her relationships with men had always been far more calculated and planned. Perhaps it was the atmosphere. A Chinook had come through that afternoon, a mass of warm air descending down the sides of the mountains and replacing the arctic chill that had inhabited Calgary for the last month. Chinooks were a phenomena that Tamara had never seen before. The temperature went from frigid to balmy in less than an hour. The thin crust of snow on the front lawn melted; Kevin went out to play in a light jacket; and Jake went around the house opening the windows to let the sun's warmth come in.

It was a lovely Sunday afternoon and, if she hadn't known it was February and that Chinooks only lasted a day or two, Tamara would have thought that winter had finally unclenched its cold grip on the city. The freedom of stepping outside without a heavy coat, hat, mitts and boots was heavenly, and the deceptive aura of spring made them feel slightly giddy. Jake and Tamara took the children to the zoo, then to a muddy playground where Kevin stamped around in his rubber boots and finally out to Baskin & Robbins. Jennifer was still allergic to cow's milk so they fed her orange sherbet, and her blue eyes grew round and enormous as Tamara spooned it in her mouth. There was an unreal feel to the afternoon and a sensation that their enjoyment was some-how illegal, that they had plucked happiness from a tree reluctant to yield its fruit. The mood stayed with them right through dinner, the children's bedtime and afterwards when they sat together in the living room sipping at Guy's Corvoisier Brandy and talking.

The conversation meandered along lazy lines. Jake told Tamara how he had met Guy and his family; Tamara talked about the theatre. They didn't touch on any sensitive topics, and the feeling that arose between them was warm, cosy and friendly. Now that Tamara had decided not to dislike Jake, she couldn't find anything about him that wasn't pleasant. In fact, she was finding that his lack of urban sophistication—at least her definition of it—was refreshing. He was very different from the men she had known in New York. He wasn't obsessed with glitter, with fame, with gossip or with the acquisition of luxury and elegance. He wasn't self-centred; he didn't indulge in moods; and he didn't strain to be brittle and clever. There was something very natural and masculine about Jake that Tamara found very appealing.

So, of course, she shouldn't have been surprised. There had been an undercurrent of sexuality in the air all day. They had smiled at one another and touched one another, their hands meeting as they passed Jennifer back and forth. Tamara knew enough about men to recognise Jake's desire to go to bed with her, but she hadn't acknowledged it. Maybe being pregnant had dulled her reflexes; maybe she had begun to believe that pregnancy and celibacy automatically went together; maybe underneath she had believed that no man would want to make love to a woman whose body was swollen with another man's child.

Whatever the reasons, Tamara had gone to bed with no other thought in her mind except that of sleep after a wonderful day. She had brushed her hair and her teeth, pulled on a lighter nightgown than the one she usually wore and climbed into bed. The baby kicked like mad for a few minutes, and she wondered whether she was going to have one of those wakeful nights that had started to occur with greater and greater frequency. But 'it'—as Tamara had dubbed the foetus—calmed down, and she was able to curl over on her side and think dreamily about how nice the day had been. She was just dozing off when a body slipped next to hers and she felt a strong arm encircle the rounded curve of her waistline.

'Jake?'

'Mmmm—you mind?'

'Well, I . . .' It was hard to mind the warm feel of his hand caressing her skin, running up the slope of her abdomen and gently cupping the fullness of her breast. There was a lazy sensuality to his motions, a sureness, and a lack of intensity that was comforting.

There was a warm growl in his voice. 'I've wanted to do this all day.'

'You have?'

'You didn't guess.'

'Well, now that I think about it . . .'

He was now pulling up her nightgown so that his palm rested directly on her flesh. 'You feel good.'

'Have you ever made love to a pregnant lady?'

'No—have you ever made love to a pregnant gentleman?'

Tamara laughed and turned so that she was

facing Jake. His face was a pale oval in the darkness, and he was naked. When she put her hand on his waist, she could feel the smoothness of his muscles, bone and skin.

'The baby's going to get in the way,' she said.

He stroked her abdomen with both hands. 'Solid, isn't it?'

'Very.'

'What's this?'

'My belly-button. What did you think it was?'

'It's sticking out a mile and a half.'

Tamara put mock-reproach in her voice. 'That's not very flattering.'

'It's no worse than an erection.'

'Oh?' she asked archly. 'Is that sticking out a mile and a half, too?'

His voice was low, seductive. 'That's for me to know and you to find out.'

Her fingers lightly and teasingly stroked the whorl of hair at his belly. 'I never thought of you as a man of mystery.' He pushed her slightly so that she was lying on her back and then he put his arms around so that he could drew her closer to him. 'On second thought,' she added, feeling the hardness of him against her leg, 'you're not mysterious at all.'

'I'm an open book,' he declared, nuzzling her neck.

'Actually, this wasn't predictable.'

'What?'

'You and me—ending up in bed together.'

'Oh—I don't know. There was always something there.'

'Dislike, hatred, antipathy.'

'An awareness of one another.'

'That's true.' She stared up at the ceiling. 'We'll never get along, you know.'

Jake propped himself up on his elbow and stared down at her. Even in the darkness, her hair caught the stray rays of light and reflected their lustre in a deep orange glow. 'Tamara, we haven't even tried yet!'

She waved a ghostly hand in the air. 'That's just sex.'

'What do you mean—just sex?'

'You know.'

'No, I don't. There's different kinds of sex, some of it's terrible and some of it's great.'

Tamara wasn't sure that there was such a thing as great sex, not that she was going to tell Jake that. 'I don't think we can have a relationship.'

'You mean living together?'

'Yes. I don't do that; it's too . . . confining. I like my independence.'

Jake slipped his hand over a breast and gently caressed the nipple. 'That's fine with me. I'm not one for commitment either.'

Tamara sighed a bit as her nipple rose between his fingers and that first sensation of desire curled in her groin. 'Just so you know.'

'Mmmm.' Jake didn't bother answering her. He had pulled up her nightgown and bent his head so that he could kiss her breasts, first one and then the other, licking each in turn.

Tamara idly ran her fingers through the thick coarse strands of his hair. 'You were very disparaging about them, you know.'

'About what?'

'My breasts.'

'I was?'

'In a subtle sort of way. I think you referred to me as "scrawny".'

He ran a finger under one breast and around its side to her armpit. 'You've improved.'

'It's the pregnancy. I was never very big to begin with.'

There was amusement in his voice. 'Are you trying to discourage me? I don't meet too many women who talk down the merchandise.'

'And all my hair is the colour of grated carrots.'

It took Jake a moment to get it, and then he roared with laughter.

'I just wanted you to know,' Tamara said primly, 'precisely what you were getting.'

'Right—one pregnant, temperamental and talkative lady.'

'I'm not ready to get down to business,' she said indignantly. '*You* may have been thinking about this all day, but I can assure you—I haven't. It never even crossed my mind.'

His voice was soft. 'I'll make sure you're ready.'

'And I don't like brute force.'

'God forbid.'

'Or someone who's in a big hurry.'

'I've got all night.'

'Or . . .'

He kissed her then and his lips were a very effective silencer. They had never kissed before so his mouth was new to her, softer than she would have thought, mobile and tender. He ran his tongue along the curve of her lips and across the edge of her teeth. Then he slipped it into her mouth, coaxing her lips apart and seeking out her sweet warmth. One hand crept into the curly tendrils of hair at the nape of her neck while the other began trailing a sensuous path over her breasts and up the silky slope of her stomach. It had started down its descent when Jake suddenly lifted his head.

'There's life in there,' he said with surprise.

'I think you're interrupting its sleep.'

'Actually,' he grinned, 'I'm planning to enrich its environment.'

Tamara would have liked to have come back with a good retort, but the movement of Jake's fingers distracted her. He touched her hip, the place where her stomach ended and the soft curls between her legs. He stroked her more gently than any man had stroked her before, and Tamara could feel the rush of heat, the spreading damp, her own gradual opening to those silent questing fingers. The pregnancy seemed to have made her fuller and more sensitive, and the sensations he was causing in her made Tamara move restlessly against the sheets, arching as best she could towards him and reaching to touch him.

'Not yet,' he said, pushing her hand away.

'Why?'

'Your turn's not over.'

His mouth replaced his hand, and Tamara's

legs fell helplessly apart. Perhaps it was the night evolving so smoothly from a relaxed day, or the fact that her pregnancy had changed the way her body felt, or Jake's obvious skill—not that a man's technique had ever particularly affected her before—whatever it was, Tamara responded to the caress of that mouth and the sliding motion of his fingers in a way she had never responded before. Desire rose up in her, blurred her mind and made her moan out loud. She, who had always known precisely what she was doing and had often faked with such a dramatic talent that no man had ever guessed her duplicity, now lost track of time and of place, her body riding a crescent wave of pleasure and sensuality, her hands clenching themselves into fists, her head turning from side to side and then back again in that almost unbearable ecstasy.

'My turn,' he said.

She made him lie flat on his back; she wouldn't let him touch her although his fingers ached for her when she began caressing him. Her hands moved over him capriciously, alighting on his chest, his belly, the top of his thighs in a seemingly random and maddeningly teasing fashion. She made circles, figures of eight, brush strokes and angled swoops. For a long time, she didn't touch him where it counted, and the heat of desire combined with a deep and clamorous aching made him groan.

'A mile and a half?' she asked innocently.

'Going for two,' he said roughly.

'Really,' she drawled. 'Maybe I should check that out.'

'It needs testing.'

The test was thorough, all encompassing and one of the most tantalising experiences of Jake's long and varied sexual career. He felt himself tightening under the ministrations of her hands and tongue, rising to the temptations of a mouth that would move away just when he thought he could stand it no longer, and swelling to the point of bursting. He want to throw Tamara on her back and plunge into her; he wanted to ease the almost painful throbbing of his penis, but he didn't dare move. Every time he made a motion beyond that of a slight arch, Tamara would stop, leaving him with an agonising sensation of unfulfilment.

'Where the hell did you learn that?' he asked huskily.

'St Margaret Mary's School for Girls in Fairfax, New York.'

'Jesus.'

Tamara never knew exactly how long they made love. It could have been for hours. She only knew that they traded turns until neither of them could stand another moment of foreplay. They talked, whispered and laughed their way through physical and verbal teasing and a small argument about final positions. When they finally joined together, she was on the top, her knees on the bed, her hands on his shoulders. He came first, arching beneath her, and she followed soon after with an orgasm that was deep, profound, overwhelming and body-shaking. It was also frightening; in fact, it frightened both of them because her uterus went into a contraction at the same time, her abdomen becoming rockhard against Jake's belly. They both felt it at the same time and, for a second, neither breathed. Then it dissipated and Tamara sighed, her shoulders slumping.

'Tam, are you okay? Is the baby okay?'

'I think so.'

'Did it hurt? Do you think it was labour?'

'No, it didn't hurt at all.' She slipped off him, still slightly shaky from having made love, and lay down carefully on the bed, her hands encompassing the mass of her stomach. 'And if it was a labour pain, I think it should hurt, don't you?'

He gathered her into his arms. 'I'm not a doctor, honey.'

'You woke the baby up, anyway.'

'I was just rocking his boat.'

Tamara felt the small thumps beneath her fingers and felt reassured by their vigour. 'I think he liked it,' she said, smiling. 'He's developed a certain rhythm.'

Jake kissed her on the temple and then the ear. 'Did you?' he asked softly.

'Did I what?'

'Like it.'

Tamara was rarely shy, but now she discovered that she couldn't speak. How could she tell Jake what sex had been like for her in the past, and how unusual it was for her to get any particular pleasure out of the act? She had become very adept at pleasing men and almost incapable at pleasing herself. She had never known how to tell a man what she liked and, more often than not, sex was merely the interlude between a fascinating flirtation and a night spent with someone's arms warding off the demons of loneliness. Tamara had never in her life gone to bed with a man for the sole purpose of satisfying a sexual urge, or because she had been overwhelmingly swayed by passion. In fact, there had always been another Tamara looking on, an outside being who watched her sexual proceedings with a jaded, bored and mocking air. Despite a hundred lovers, Tamara had never once lost herself in the act of love.

But tonight had been different; Jake had been different. He had laughed and joked his way through the awkwardness that always came when lovers are new to one another. He had been so relaxed that she, in turn, had fallen in with the motions, the feelings and the sensations of pleasure. And he had known with an unerring accuracy what she had wanted. Tamara had merged with his sensuality, yielded to it and, for the first time in years, been satisfied by it. Of course, she had liked it, but there seemed no way of telling that to Jake without baring the skeleton of frigidity hidden in her mental closet. So all Tamara could do was murmur appreciatively and, with soft kisses, let Jake know just how pleased she had been.

'How about a repeat performance?' he asked.

Tamara stopped kissing him. 'Tonight!'

'Or tomorrow or the day after that.'

'Well, it was . . . nice.'

'Listen, lover, we'll try it again, but you have to talk to the doctor first. I don't want to hurt you.'

'Oh.'

'Promise me you'll call him tomorrow.'

'All right.'

'Otherwise, I'll cut you off.'

'You wouldn't do that,' she said.

His voice was threatening. 'Oh, yes, I would. Even if you begged, even if you crawled on your hands and knees, even if you promised me . . .' He paused.

'What?'

'I don't know. Do you have any more tricks?'

Tamara smiled into the darkness and rubbed her cheek against Jake's shoulder. 'That's for me to know,' she teased, 'and you to find out.'

The doctor told Tamara that sex during pregnancy was healthy, not to worry about contractions which were normal for a uterus during orgasm, and the main thing was that she should be comfortable. He also added, with a smile in his voice, that the best part was that she didn't have to worry about birth control. The week that followed this advice was the most unique and wonderful of Tamara's life. The children seemed to be on their best behaviour, the weather stayed relatively mild even after the Chinook had gone, and every night was a romantic fantasy come true. Once the children were in bed, the lights turned off and the doors locked, Jake would join

Tamara beneath the demure bedspread of bonneted and parasoled girls. There, they talked, laughed and made love. There, Tamara learned that there was far more to sex than she had ever known. She had always thought of lovemaking in terms of technique, of skill, of experience. The casual sex that she had indulged in had usually taken place under the influence of alcohol or drugs and in the guise of an intimacy that had never really existed. When a lover had been a stranger only a few hours before, the conversation was often awkward, the laughter forced and the fumbling embarrassing. With Jake, Tamara discovered that sex could be fun.

Of course, they had absolutely nothing in common; that she ascertained almost immediately. Jake cheerfully confessed that he didn't know Pinter from Albee, preferred movies to plays and, in general, enjoyed comedy and an action adventure to anything with a solemn theme. His taste in art was predictably abysmal, and he had far too much paperwork in his office to have time to read novels. He skimmed several different papers and magazines a week; *The Calgary Herald*, *The Financial Post*, *Barron's*, *Newsweek* and *Penthouse*.

'*Penthouse*,' exclaimed Tamara in disgust. 'Women with breasts siliconed to the size of beach balls.'

Jake gave her an unrepentant grin. 'A man needs a bit of stimulation occasionally.'

'Are you implying I'm not stimulation enough?'

'Look—see how stimulated I am.'

'Besides, it gives a girl an inferiority complex.'

Jake stroked one soft, unfettered breast. 'Nothing inferior here,' he flattered. 'Nicest golf ball I've felt all day . . . Ouch! You really know how to pinch. Is that what they taught you in acting school?'

'And that, too.'

'Mmmm—I know they didn't teach you *that* on Broadway.'

'You're a glutton for punishment.'

'Punish me,' he pleaded, whispering in her ear. 'Please punish me.'

Their affair seemed to thrive on their differences and was nurtured in an environment of such domesticity that Tamara wondered secretly if both she and Jake weren't frauds. They had both agreed that neither wanted families in the ordinary sense of the word, and both were opposed to making any binding form of commitment. This left them free to perform in a setting so parochial, mundane and humdrum that it was laughable. Jake acted like a father to the children, and Tamara was the mother. They bathed the kids, fed them, scolded them and played with them. They went grocery shopping, washed dishes and made beds. The only thing they didn't have to do was pay the bills; those accumulated in a pile on Guy's desk, awaiting his return from Mexico.

The closer Rebecca's and Guy's return came, the more giddy Jake and Tamara became. They couldn't decide how to confront the McLarens

with the *fait accompli* of a full-blown love affair
—not that they used the word 'love'. That had
been excised out of their vocabulary early on.
They were solidly in agreement that what they
were indulging in was a temporary fling made all
the more interesting by Tamara's pregnancy,
their earlier animosity and their differences.
Tamara had every intention, she told Jake, of
returning to New York after the baby was born
and resuming her interrupted acting career. And
Jake, in turn, assured her that he was happiest
when his bachelorhood was not being threatened
by some insecure female who was looking not
only for a bedmate, but also a lifelong marital
partnership.

This mutually agreed-upon future ensured a
comfortable feeling of unrestricted freedom, and
the chance for both of them to act just as they
pleased. They could talk on any subject, dress
sloppily if they cared to and disagree violently if
the topic warranted it. They debated the relative
values of rural versus urban living, Calgary
versus New York, sophistication versus being
natural. Their discussion on roles of women in
society caused Tamara to call Jake 'a sentimental
male chauvinist pig', after he had admitted that
he thought a woman should stay home with her
children, while Jake, after listening to Tamara talk
about the past men in her life, informed her that
underneath she was a 'manhater to the core'. The
sex that they had after that conversation was fast,
furious, rough almost to the point of brutality,
and very satisfying to both of them.

The day before the plane from Mexico was due back, Jake packed his suitcase and returned to his apartment. Although there was an unspoken assumption that they would probably resume sexual relations after Guy and Rebecca had returned, neither of them actually said anything about a time or a place or a meeting. That night was the first that Tamara had slept alone in over a week, and she discovered that she didn't like it. The bed seemed wide and empty and cold. She had nobody to warm her feet on or snuggle up against. She tossed and turned, discussed the situation with 'it', who was also wide-awake and performing an intricate set of gymnastics, and finally gave up. By the time she called Jake it was three o'clock in the morning.

'I can't sleep,' she said.

'Me either.'

'Whose idea was this anyway?'

'Yours—you said the house should be back to normal.'

'I didn't say that—you did.'

He gave a low laugh. 'I think you miss me.'

There was a pout in her voice. 'My feet are cold.'

'Get the heating pad.'

'The bed's too big.'

'Tuck Kevin's teddy bear in next to you.'

'I can't relax.'

'Well, if I were there, I would . . .'

'Oh, no, you don't,' she returned quickly. 'I don't believe in making love over the telephone.'

'I've spoiled you,' he said. 'I can tell.'

'Spoiled rotten,' she agreed mournfully.

'A little deprivation will be good for you. By the time I see you again, you'll be insatiable. You'll tear my shirt off, you'll rip my trousers, you'll . . .'

'Dreamer.'

Jake gave a mock sigh. 'I've always wanted to be a sex object. I want women to drool over me, ogle my body, use me in their fantasies. My main ambition in life is to be a centrefold.'

'The staple will pinch.' Her voice was tart.

'What staple?'

'The one in your navel.'

There was a choking sound. 'Tamara, go to sleep. I have to work tomorrow and Jennifer will be up bright and chipper at six.'

'What am I going to tell Rebecca?'

'You don't have to tell her anything.'

'You don't know her. She'll nudge and nag me until I do.'

'So tell her.'

'Then I'll hear a litany of I-told-you-so's.'

'Well, she did think we'd make the perfect match.'

'Do we?' she whispered.

His voice was serious, sombre. 'Tam, I don't think I've ever enjoyed a woman in bed so much.'

A lump was rising in her throat. 'Even the golf balls?'

'Golf balls, hell. They've graduated to tennis.'

'Jake?'

'What?'

'There aren't a whole lot of men who would find a pregnant woman sexy.'

'They don't know what they're missing. The lump in the middle is the best part of all.'

'I wish you were here,' she whispered.

'So do I, darling. So do I.'

Guy and Rebecca returned with suitcases overflowing with Mexican souvenirs and the most beautiful tans Tamara had ever seen. Kevin ran into their arms, but Jennifer wasn't sure what to do at first. She looked from Rebecca to Tamara and then back again before finally stretching out her arms to her mother. Rebecca gave her daughter a baleful look and then blew bubbles into her neck, making Jennifer laugh and grab at her hair. The unpacking of the suitcases was ceremoniously done in the living room, and soon every surface was littered with embroidered tops, engraved leather items, silver jewellery and billowy cotton dresses with coloured designs. Tamara received an intricately carved silver necklace with turquoise insets that matched the colour of her eyes, a white overblouse with lace patterns on it and a small silver baby rattle.

'For the future,' Rebecca said.

Tamara looked down at it and tried to imagine her own baby holding on to it. She couldn't envision it, couldn't translate the lumps and bumps in her abdomen into a tiny fist. She lifted it up and shook it gently, hearing the beads inside rattle against the silver.

Kevin had a leather donkey almost large

enough to ride, and he sat on it with a sombrero on his head. 'Go, horsie,' he cried.

Guy squatted down beside him. 'That's a burro.'

'I saw a burro on television,' Kevin announced proudly.

'You did? When?'

'On *Sesame Street*. When I had the chicken-pox.'

There was a sudden silence in the living room, and both Guy and Rebecca looked at Tamara who was now busily studying the rattle in her hand.

'Chicken-pox?' Guy asked.

'And Uncle Jake had them, too. And Jennifer. We all had the chicken-poxes. But Aunt Tam said I shouldn't tell you because you'd worry a lot and want to come home.'

Guy said to Tamara, 'When did this happen?'

She looked up and gave them a careful smile. 'The day after you left.'

Guy said, 'What did you do to Kevin to keep him quiet? Bribe him?' and Kevin asked, 'What does bribe mean, Daddy?'

Rebecca, meanwhile, gave Tamara a scolding look. 'I should have guessed. I knew those phone calls were fishy. Well, tell all. How bad was it?'

'Well, Kevin was covered, Jennifer got off easy and Jake was a disaster.'

Guy started to laugh. 'Imagine Jake having the chicken-pox.'

'Oh, Daddy,' Kevin piped up, 'he was really sick and itchy. He even took more baths than me.'

Rebecca gave Tamara a look that was still suspicious. 'Is that why Jake was staying here?'

Tamara nodded. 'I played a gracious Florence Nightingale. You would have been proud of me, Becks. I took temperatures, soothed fevered brows, gave medication and changed more beds than I'll probably change for the rest of my lifetime.'

'Did you . . . ?'

Rebecca never finished her sentence. Prudence made her cut it off midway; Guy was there, and Kevin with his big ears and even greater propensity for blurting out the wrong thing at the wrong time. Tamara hoped the Florence Nightingale camouflage would work, but she knew better. When Rebecca was on the trail of something clandestine, you couldn't get her off until she had discovered exactly what you were concealing. Tamara had vivid memories of childhood incidents when her sister with unerring accuracy had uncovered her cache of candy, found a hidden message, hounded her until she revealed the hideout of a secret club. The only thing Rebecca had never been able to get out of her was the reason behind her final argument with Martine —the one that had forced her to leave home at seventeen, never to return.

So, she wasn't surprised when Rebecca caught her alone the following day when Guy had gone to work, Kevin was in school and Jennifer was taking a nap. She came into the bedroom where Tamara was reading, sat down on the chair beside the bed and fixed her with a shrewd and insistent look.

'Okay,' she challenged, 'out with it.'

'With what?' Tamara replied innocently.

'What went on here with Jake.'

Tamara knew she was going to have to spill the beans, but it was still fun to drag out the suspense. 'Jake?'

'Blond, six feet tall.'

'Oh—that Jake.'

'Listen, Tam, I figured it out last night. If Kevin got the chicken-pox the day after we left, and the incubation period is a week, then chances are that Jennifer and Jake probably came down with it together. Kevin told me that he didn't leave until just before we got home. I don't have to be a mathematical genius to figure out that he stayed here a week beyond his bout of chicken-pox.'

'Becks, you missed your calling,' Tamara exclaimed with admiration. 'You should have been in the detective business.'

Rebecca ignored her. 'So . . . ?'

Tamara threw her hands up in the air. 'Okay, okay. We slept together.'

'Oh, Tam,' Rebecca breathed, leaning forward intently, 'I knew it. I just *knew* it.'

'We're not getting married. We're only having an affair.'

'Still,' Rebecca laughed with delight, 'I've always thought that you and Jake would get along once you stopped being so prejudiced about one another.'

'Well,' Tamara smiled, a hint of amusement in her voice, 'I guess you could call it "getting along".'

But Rebecca refused to be pulled into a humorous contemplation of Tamara's affair with Jake. Her smile slowly disappeared and, giving Tamara a serious look, she leaned back in her chair. 'I hope you'll treat him well,' she said.

Tamara gave her a glance of astonishment. 'What does that mean?'

'It means that he can't be . . . handled the way your other lovers were. He's too gentle, too soft, too kind.'

'Handled? Handled how?'

'You know.'

'No, I don't.'

'Tam, you never cared about any of them. You treated them like dirt. If one left, another took his place and you could barely tell the difference.'

'Isn't that a bit of an exaggeration?'

'Please, Tam,' Rebecca begged, 'don't do it to him. It would hurt him so much. He's a man with a big heart and . . . if he gives it to you . . .'

'You're jumping the gun. We're friends, that's all.'

But Rebecca wasn't listening. 'If you have his heart,' she explained, 'you'll be holding it in the palm of your hand, and all it takes . . .' She held one hand palm upwards with the fingers bent as if it were holding something precious and, in a symbolic motion, snapped it into a tightly clenched fist. '. . . is that, and you'll break him—*just like that*.'

CHAPTER NINE

THE seventh and eighth months of Tamara's pregnancy went by in a dream-like sort of sequence. At first, she spent her weekdays with Guy and Rebecca, her weekends with Jake, but eventually the ratio of time spent with the McLarens and Jake reversed itself. Although she and Jake had once agreed that they had no intention of living together, that agreement seemed to have less and less value as the days went by. As she neared the end of her eighth month, Tamara spent only the afternoons with Rebecca, having moved completely in with Jake, puttering around his apartment, knitting him a sweater (she had finally made so many baby sweaters that Rebecca had suggested she try something bigger), getting up with him in the morning before he went to work and falling asleep after he left. She would wake up in time to make some lunch for the two of them and then she would either go for a doctor's appointment, her pre-natal exercise class or visit Rebecca. She would be back home in time for dinner and was often nodding off to sleep by nine o'clock. As the foetus grew bigger, stronger and more active, Tamara found herself becoming slower, sleepier and quieter than she had ever been.

She and Jake often made love when he came

home from lunch. She was at her liveliest then, when the afternoon sun would angle across Jake's wide bed and catch them in whatever position they had taken to accommodate Tamara's growing pregnancy. She learned, during this time, that there were many different tempos to making love. Sometimes they were lazy and slow; sometimes Jake took her with an abandon that was just this side of being rough; sometimes she took him, teasing him the way he liked, pampering him, playing with him in a way she had never really played with another man. No other relationship that she had ever had allowed for this development of intimacy. Her affairs had always ended after a few nights or perhaps at the most after a month. She had never had enough time to discover what sex could really be like.

And the physical intimacies went further than mere sexual ones. Her stomach played tricks on her and she could no longer eat fried or spiced foods. Jake was very sweet about this. Since she was a rotten cook, he would plan menus, go shopping and cook up meals that were bland but, he hoped, intriguing. She woke up frequently at night, the causes ranging from the activity of the baby, the need to visit the bathroom, a lower back ache, to muscle cramps in her legs. Jake talked to her until the baby calmed down, rubbed her back, massaged her calves. He had wonderfully warm and strong hands and a seemingly unlimited source of patience. Sometimes Tamara wondered why he had never married and had a wife and children of his own to care for. There was certainly a part of Jake that was at odds with his philosophy of freedom. His apartment, for example, was cosy, homely and inviting. It didn't have that feeling of being a motel that some bachelors' apartments had: a place to sleep, eat and leave. It had deep, comfortable chairs, many pictures and knick-knacks, a kitchen designed for real cooking with double ovens, racks of spices, a shelf of well-worn and dog-eared cookbooks.

No, she thought, the image of Jake as playboy didn't fit in with his apartment. He didn't have a stereo system by his bed or a Jacuzzi in his bathroom. He kept his drink in an antique sideboard in the dining room and didn't have a martini shaker anywhere. The mythical appurtenances of the carefree single male; the fur bedspread, the mirrors on the walls, the latest in modern stereo technology, were missing and, in their stead, were newspapers, magazines, an extraordinary collection of jazz records and a cupboard that held such healthy baking products as bran, wheat germ and nuts. Tamara hadn't known what to make of it when she spent her first weekend with Jake, but it had come to her slowly and without any doubts that, underneath the seemingly casual bachelor façade, was a man deeply committed to the comforts of domesticity.

Not that they ever discussed it or the child to come or the future in any specific way. The assumption underlying their relationship was that it was temporary and that, since the both of them were acknowledged hedonists, the

pleasure of the moment was more important than
any consideration of what might happen in a
month's time. That way neither Tamara nor Jake
felt threatened by what was happening between
them. They lived together because it was convenient; they ate together because it was more
fun to eat with someone than be alone; and they
slept together because the sex was mutually
satisfying and because an early morning hug was
one of the world's loveliest experiences. This was
what they said to one another and agreed upon.
What they didn't say, however, would have
filled an enormous book.

Tamara didn't tell Jake about the dreams; she
didn't think he would have liked them. Some
were sometimes frightening; others were extremely comforting. The ones in which she
dreamed of childbirth terrified her. She never, in
these dreams, had the baby the normal way; she
was always being cut open or torn apart. Strange
hands touched her body intimately; strangers
took the baby out of her and put it away in places
she couldn't find or reach. Sometimes she had the
baby in a hospital, but more often than not she
found herself in other places; underground garages, dirty factories, deep in the woods just before winter was about to set in, lying on a bed of
old, crackling leaves that scratched her cold, bare
skin. The imagined pain was either excruciat-
ing or completely absent. None of it made the
slightest sense so Tamara never mentioned these
dreams to Jake. What was the point?

And the comforting dreams occasionally made

up for the bad ones. In these she was extremely happy because the baby had a place to sleep. She never knew where this small crib actually was, the dream only focussed on the bed itself. It was pale yellow and had slender, carved bars. The sheets were a soft white with tiny, yellow animals on them and a mobile of unicorns in shades of blue and purple waved above them. In this dream, she was always rearranging a comforter on the bed. Rebecca had made it, there were girls with parasols on it. Over and over again, she folded the comforter, setting it down, plumping it up, knowing the baby would sleep under it. The dream was pleasant and soothing and Tamara knew precisely what it all meant. The crib symbolised a home and that comforter was— what else?—a subconscious desire for soothing, maternal comforts. Tamara suspected that it wasn't the baby who was supposed to sleep in that lovely crib. It was herself.

But she didn't tell Jake about this dream either. Dreams weren't real life, and subconscious desires often contradicted conscious ones. Of course, Tamara understood her need to feel secure, she felt the same as any woman who was about to be responsible for a helpless infant. In her case, this need was magnified by the precarious life she led in New York. She wasn't sure how she would feed and take care of a baby while trying to earn a living and still pursue her acting career. The only thing she knew was that other women did it. There must be thousands of single mothers in Manhattan alone, and they managed.

Tamara was confident that she would, too. She had, after all, left home when she was a teenager and survived in the world's toughest urban jungle. She didn't think there was anything that she couldn't handle if she put her mind to it. She had, therefore, decided to have the baby in Calgary and stay until it was about three months old. By that time, she would have got her strength back, the baby would be on a more or less normal schedule and she would be ready to tackle the world once again.

And, when she and Jake accidentally touched upon the future, this was the sort of thing they discussed in passing—her plans, his trip to the Arctic during the summer, whether he would trade in his jeep for something more compact. These were safe topics, the kind that were abstract, unemotional and non-entangling. They left both Jake and Tamara with the chance for a quick get-away, should either of them feel the need to go. It was like living in a room that had two exits with the doors partially open. There were no locks and keys, no bolts and chains, no sense of suffocation. It suited Tamara just fine and, from the way Jake behaved, it seemed to suit him as well. They even mentioned it occasionally, smiling at one another as if exchanging congratulations for an arrangement that was so perfect.

The arrival of Sheila's letter only served to confirm Tamara's belief that Calgary held no future for her. Sheila wrote in a breezy style about a new lover, 'tall, dark, handsome and shallow,' the problems of her new apartment, 'leaky plumbing,' and sexual harassment on her job, 'never work in the garment industry—the buyers think that the secretaries are as pinchable as the models. My rear is black and blue after the last showing.' It was a chatting letter, full of gossip about people Tamara had forgotten and rumours of new plays and productions. It was the latter that caught Tamara's interest, and one item in particular made her sit up with a sudden feeling of anticipation. A producer that both she and Sheila knew was talking about a revival of *Medea*. 'Of course,' Sheila wrote, 'he's having the typical problems of money so it's all very much in the talking stages. Still, Bob is tenacious about these things, and I expect he'll eventually get somewhere. Wouldn't that be a perfect role for you? I've always thought that Medea would be a redhead.'

Just the thought of playing Medea made Tamara shiver. It was a great role, designed for an actress of great personality and power. She told Jake about it that night after the letter had come when they were lying in bed together.

'Medea,' he said musingly. 'A Greek woman. You know I'm an uncultured slob. Fill me in.'

'She's a mythical character from ancient times. Medea had magical powers and, because she was in love with Jason, she helped him and the Argonauts get the Golden Fleece. I think she even killed her brother in the process. She had two children by Jason and he promised to marry her, but when they got back to Greece . . .'

'He skipped out and she sued him for child support.'

Tamara pinched him. 'Don't be irreverent; Zeus will strike you down with a thunderbolt. Anyway, Jason decided to marry the daughter of the king of Corinth and his betrayal made Medea so furious that she killed the princess and then, when Jason came after her, she killed the two children she had by him.'

'Talk about a bloodthirsty lady.'

'The story's been done in a play by Euripides.'

'And that's the play this guy wants to produce?'

'Yes—it's very powerful, a wonderful vehicle for an actress.'

'I wouldn't think Greek revivals are very popular or profitable.'

'They can be if they're done well, they appeal to the high-brow types and, besides, the critics love them.'

'And you think you could do it?'

Tamara took a deep breath and clenched her hands together. 'I'd love a crack at it; it's such a wonderful role. Just the chance to audition for it would be an experience.'

'Wouldn't your producer friend want a big name for the part?'

'It depends on who's around and what Bob's concept of the play is. Everyone will have a chance to try out and, if I can convince him, he might be willing to go with me. I've known Bob for a long time; in fact, I did a part in a play he had off-Broadway. We got along, and he said any time he had another production he'd like to see me again. That kind of connection is really important, Jake. Like everything else—it's not only what you know but who you know.'

'How long will it take this guy to get a production together?'

'Six months,' Tamara answered. 'It depends on how long it takes him to get backing.'

Jake's voice was careful. 'So you might make it back to New York in time.'

'Uh-uh.'

'That's great,' he said.

'It is, isn't it?'

'I guess it would be a real break for you.'

Tamara was too excited about the prospects of playing the part of Medea to hear anything but the content of Jake's words. 'It would be fantastic,' she continued happily. 'I could have any part I wanted after that. You see, Medea is such a powerful woman and her life is so tragic. She's madly in love with Jason; she's crazy about him, and when he betrays her, she's the epitome of "the woman scorned". He doesn't want her any more and offers her money instead of marriage. Her love turns to a hate so profound and so angry that she kills her children. Can you imagine killing your own children as revenge?'

'No.'

'It's a wonderful role, Jason.'

There was a funny pause and then, 'Jake—I'm Jake.'

Tamara gave an uneasy laugh. 'I'm sorry . . . I guess I was already so involved with the story

that I was already Medea in my own mind.' She
rolled over to put her arms around him and
discovered that he was lying there very stiffly,
staring up into the dark of the ceiling. She ran one
hand over his chest, rubbed it gently over the
whorl of hair at his belly and delicately traversed
the soft bud of his penis. 'I wouldn't forget you,'
she added in an arch, teasing tone. 'I think we've
met before.'

There was a brief second when she wasn't sure
whether she had insulted Jake beyond redemp-
tion, but then he was taking her up in his arms
and growling into the curve of her neck. 'You
only *think* we've met before?'

'I surrender,' she said, laughing with relief.
'We've met before.'

'Damn right,' he growled. 'And don't forget it.'

Tamara pressed her cheek against his and
nibbled at the lobe of his ear. 'I couldn't,' she
whispered. 'You're unforgettable.'

In the first week of her ninth month, Tamara
went into a false labour. Not that she thought it
was false. It felt and acted much like the real
thing, and it frightened her. She woke up at about
two in the morning with pains in her lower back
that came periodically and then disappeared. She
could feel her uterus contract and then relax
along with each pain. She stared into the dark,
prayed that the pains would go away and
worried. The baby would be premature; she
was terrified of hospitals; she didn't like doctors,
not even her kindly obstetrician; and the thought

of actually giving birth scared her silly. All the details of her childbirth nightmares came back to haunt her. Finally, after an hour of sporadic pains and contractions, she shook Jake awake.

'I think I'm having the baby,' she said in a tremulous voice.

He was sleepy and groggy. 'What?'

'The baby. I think it's coming.'

He sat up abruptly then and switched on the lamp that sat on a night-table beside the bed. Both of them blinked as light flooded the bedroom, and they stared at one another. Jake's hair was tousled and the skin around his eyes was creased from sleep. Tamara's orange curls were wild and tangled. In her fear, she had gone pale and her freckles stood out on her cheeks like pale-brown polka dots.

'You're having labour pains?'

'About every ten minutes.'

'I thought the doctor said you still had a couple of weeks to go.'

'He did.'

'Babies have been known to come early, haven't they?'

Tamara nodded and clenched her hands together. 'But I'm frightened. I really am.'

He took her fists between his hands. 'Well, that's understandable. You don't have a baby every day.'

Her teeth had started to chatter now. 'This is worse than an audition. Or an opening night. Oh, God.'

'Tam, women do it every day.'

'Don't give me that stuff about Chinese peasants.'

He gave her an astonished look. 'What Chinese peasants?'

'You know, the ones who work in the rice paddy, come in during coffee break to have a baby and then go back to planting.'

Jake started to laugh. 'Coffee break?'

Shivering had set in. 'I don't know,' she went on miserably. 'A *sake* break then.'

Jake pulled her next to him so that she was encircled in his arms, his bare chest hard and warm against her cheek. He gently patted her shoulder as if she were a small child. 'You'll do just fine, you know. You don't even have to rehearse any lines.'

'It's gonna hurt.'

'I never thought you'd be such a coward.'

'I am,' she wailed and then gave a slight gasp.

'Tam! What is it? A labour pain?'

She nodded, breathed lightly through the slowly growing pain, its rise to a crescendo and then its falling off, remembering the instructions in her pre-natal class. When it was over, she slumped against Jake. 'It's gone.'

His arms were tight around her. 'What did the doctor say?'

'To go to the hospital when they were strong and steady.'

'Are they?'

'I don't know,' she replied. She felt helpless and lost. It didn't seem to matter that she had read all the pregnancy books and knew all the terms and procedures by heart. The abstract knowledge didn't mean a thing when it came down to the reality of having her body take over, its dominance leaving her out of control and dependent. She didn't know what she would have done without the warm circle of Jake's arms, his calming voice, the hand steadily patting her shoulder with a soothing, relaxing rhythm. She sighed and said, 'I can't tell.'

'I'll time them,' he offered.

'It's a good thing I packed the suitcase yesterday,' she added. 'I must have had ESP.'

They were at the hospital at five that morning, and Tamara was admitted by a sleepy clerk into the maternity section. They didn't want to let Jake into the labour room, because he wasn't Tamara's husband and he wasn't listed on her records as even the next of kin, but she screamed and yelled, insisted that he was the father of the baby and, in general, made herself so obnoxious that the head nurse finally relented. Tamara was as sweet as a pussycat after that, but she could tell from the looks that the hospital staff gave one another that they thought she was slightly crazy. That didn't bother her a bit; neither did Jake's dry comment, 'That was a performance.'

She smiled at him. 'Just a small amount of New York chutzpah.'

'You've shocked them right down to the core of their Canadian souls.'

'I don't care,' she returned defiantly. 'I discovered that I didn't want to have this baby all by myself. I've even decided that you should be in the delivery room.'

'Have you now.'

'Jake, please. Don't leave me.' He was sitting by the bed and, taking his hand, she gripped it hard. 'I promise I'll be nice to everyone and not scream and be a model maternity case.'

Jake's voice was understandably hesitant. 'I don't know if I'm prepared for the delivery room.'

'Don't look, close your eyes. Just hold my hand and I'll be your willing slave.' Her voice was light, but it masked her real emotions. The Tamara of the gutsy remarks and fearless bravado had discovered that she had no courage when it came to physical discomfort. And the pain of labour was unlike anything she had experienced before. It hurt worse than a toothache, a cut or a stubbed toe. It started in her lower back, twisted into her abdomen and then sharpened itself into a dozen cutting knives.

'Hmmm,' Jake said, his voice also light and teasing. 'If I remember correctly, sex is *verboten* for six weeks after the baby comes.'

'That's just plain old ordinary sex. I'll be creative; I'll have imagination; I'll . . .' Another pain came, and Tamara gripped Jake's hand so tightly he could feel the bones crunch together. 'Please,' she begged faintly.

She was panting slightly, her face had gone quite pale, and beads of sweat dotted her upper lip. The pain was so obviously strong and overpowering that, for a brief second, Jake imagined that he too could feel it, as if their two skins and the space between them were no longer barriers and they shared the same network of veins and nerves. He also felt her panic and that desolate fear of being alone. 'All right,' he reassured her.

'Thank you,' she said fervently. 'I love you. I really do.'

The words were tossed off and, of course, Tamara had uttered them under the stress of an unusual situation, but a funny look crossed Jake's face. A vulnerable look that twisted his broad features for a second and then disappeared as if it had never existed. Tamara hadn't seen it; she was lying back against the pillow, her eyes closed, resting after her body's violence. When the doctor arrived, having been briefed on Tamara's condition and Jake's presence, he smiled to himself and thought they looked like any other couple about to have a baby for the first time; the woman drawn and tired, the man worried and strained.

The examination was brief and the consultation with the resident doctor was long. The consensus of opinion was that the labour was false and already the pains were coming at longer and longer intervals. Tamara was not dilated, and there was no other evidence that birth was imminent. 'The body just practises sometimes,' her doctor informed her and, later that morning, his words were confirmed. Her pains disappeared altogether, and Tamara was released from the hospital, feeling embarrassed and silly, even though the resident doctor had assured her,

several times over, that they were used to
mothers with false labour. It happened, he said,
all the time.

'I'm sorry,' she apologised miserably to Jake as
he drove back to the apartment. She was huddled
over to one corner of the front seat, her head
resting against the glass of the door window. She
was physically exhausted from being up most of
the night and emotionally exhausted from having
gone through the trauma of believing that she
was going to give birth any minute. All she
wanted to do now was crawl back into her own
bed and sleep.

Jake glanced at her and thought she looked like
an urchin, her body wrapped up in an old coat of
Rebecca's that was too large for her and her head
covered by a knitted toque with a white pom-
pom. Her hair was the only vibrant part of her, its
crinkled orange strands fanning out from under
the toque in a wide swathe on her collar. The rest
of her was spent; her face still pale with mauve
shadows beneath the eyes. 'Let's look on the
bright side,' he suggested.

'What bright side?'

'We've had a practice run. The doctor agreed
that I could be in the delivery room. And now,
you won't miss Cordelia's wedding.'

Tamara turned to him. 'I forgot all about it!'

'Shame on you—being a bridesmaid and all
that.'

'Hardly a bridesmaid.'

'You know,' Jake smiled, 'the old terms just
don't apply any more. How would you describe

an unmarried pregnant lady who assists at the marriage of a less than blushing bride of sixty-five?'

'I don't know,' replied Tamara, perking up just at the thought of watching Cordelia exchange vows with the dapper and energetic Henry, 'but I can't wait. It's going to be fun, isn't it?'

Cordelia's wedding was a smash. She and Henry were married by a minister in Guy's and Rebecca's living room and a big party was held afterwards. Kevin was a ring-bearer, an old friend of Cordelia's was the matron of honour and Henry's son was the best man. The wedding couple were both in suits; Cordelia in a pale grey silk with a mauve blouse, Henry upright in dark blue with the white tip of his van dyke beard brushing against the blue and white checks of a sprightly bow-tie. And the ceremony itself was less than solemn. When the minister rolled out the portentous words '. . . and till death do you part,' Cordelia glanced back at the assembled guests and gave them an amused look. Somehow, her expression seemed to say, the phrase just didn't have the proper impact, the awesome air of invocation, that it should have—not when the bride was sixty-five and the groom was seventy.

Tamara turned around to see if Jake had caught the joke and saw his grin. She was standing near Rebecca, with a spray of roses in her arms. Both were acting as bridesmaids and both wore dresses of a creamy silk. Rebecca's had a wide

laced collar, a pleated bodice and a flared skirt;
Tamara's had the same collar and hung from her
shoulders in a voluminous pleated tent. It was a
week since the episode of false labour, and
Tamara felt as if she had grown an inch for every
day that had passed. The weight of the baby
pulled her body forward, her back ached all the
time now and she had come to realise, she told
Jake, the purpose of the ninth month of pregnancy. It made a woman so physically miserable
that childbirth with all its pains now seemed like
a blessing.

It was an odd wedding with the bridal pair both
grandparents and a bridesmaid in an advanced
state of pregnancy, but it worked all the same.
Champagne was drunk afterwards, the bridal
bouquet landed in Tamara's bulging lap, causing
a lot of laughter, and toasts, some of them ribald,
were made by several members of the family.
Guy was the only one who was formal on this
occasion and raised his glass to 'bless a union
based on maturity and experience and to welcome a new father and grandfather into the
McLaren family.' Tamara saw that Rebecca's eyes
had filled with tears during this, and she suspected that this generous welcome had not come
easily to her brother-in-law. Rebecca rarely talked
about Guy other than in the most general terms,
but Tamara knew that he was the type of man
who kept his emotions to himself. Whatever
agonies he had suffered over Henry's usurpation
of his father's place had been handled in some
private part of his soul.

There was a party afterwards, and Rebecca had used a caterer to supply the food. Tamara, who was off alcohol, spicy foods and anything fattening, could only nibble at crackers and sip on Perrier water, but the rest of the guests dug in with a gusto. And because she simply couldn't stand up any more without feeling as if her back would crack, she had seated herself on a corner of the couch and watched the action from the living room. There was the clink of glasses, the chatter of people celebrating a happy occasion and Kevin's excited voice rising over the hubbub. Jennifer had woken from her nap and was resplendent in a frothy pink dress, little socks with frilly tops and new white shoes. She had just started walking a few weeks before and was unhappy in her playpen. Rebecca had put her there to keep her out of trouble, and she was standing, her fat hands on the bars, bouncing up and down, while she repeated in a woeful chant, 'Up. Up. Up.'

Henry, who was avuncular and tended to treat Tamara like a fragile Dresden doll, sat down beside her and, patting her hand, asked in a fond voice, 'How's the bun in the oven?'

Tamara thought Henry was a card. Part of her appreciation of him came from the contrast between what she saw and what Cordelia had told her. Henry was a dandy; he fussed over his clothes. He always had a neatly folded white handkerchief in his jacket pocket and wore a perky bow-tie with a tiny pattern on it. His trousers had a military crease and, in this day of casual and convenient clothes, he wore shirts that required highly polished cuff-links. On the other hand, there were Cordelia's confidences that revealed the unclothed Henry as something of a sexual tiger. Tamara quite liked imagining neat, little Henry in the disorder of a conjugal bed. And then there were his little aphorisms and sayings.

'It's rising,' she smiled.

Jake sat down on the arm of the couch at Tamara's side. 'We're hoping,' he said, 'that it doesn't overcook.'

Henry shook his head and tch-tched. 'My first wife went to ten months with my oldest boy.'

'Don't say that,' Tamara groaned. 'I'd die.'

Cordelia now appeared. She looked radiant, her cheeks pink, her eyes glowing. She sat down next to Henry, tucked her hand possessively under his elbow, and said, 'Die of what?'

'Pregnancy.'

'Nonsense. I thought Guy would do me in, but he came one week early and was no trouble at all. From the look of you, it'll be over soon anyway.'

'We'll have to give her a coming-out party,' Henry joked.

They all groaned and Cordelia gave him a poke. 'Honestly, Henry, when will you learn?'

'You can't teach an old dog new tricks.'

'He's incurable,' Cordelia said, beaming. 'He's awful.'

But from her loving smile, it was obvious that Cordelia was quite happy with Henry. They had come back from their holiday in the Bahamas looking vigorous and fit and bursting with marriage plans. They had decided to sell both their houses and buy a condominium in the city which they would use in the summer and a winter house somewhere under a southern sun. They were very pragmatic about their plans; they had even seen a lawyer and drawn up a marital contract. Cordelia had felt very strongly that, when she died, the money that Franklin had left her should pass on to Guy. Her arrangement with Henry, therefore, encompassed a marital intimacy with financial independence.

Jake was giving Cordelia a speculative look. 'Tell me, Henry, how you managed to catch this woman. The last I heard was that she couldn't see the point of marriage. It would interfere with her tax returns.'

'She couldn't resist me,' Henry teased wickedly.

'He kept asking me,' Cordelia said. 'I got so tired of saying no, that I finally said yes.'

'It wasn't that way at all,' Henry denied, shaking his head. 'She dropped hints all over the place. I practically tripped over them.'

Cordelia smiled. 'Henry! You're such a liar.'

Jake leaned over and said in a low voice. 'I wanted to marry her, you know, but she wouldn't have me.'

Henry gave Jake a look of amused conspiracy. 'You're too young for her, boy. She needs a man of mature experience.'

'All right, you two,' Cordelia chided. 'That's enough.'

Jake winked at her. 'Afraid we'll compare notes?'

'I'm going to regret every kind word I ever said on your behalf.' She put on a scolding voice. 'Pick on someone your own age.'

'Who?'

'Tamara, of course.'

Tamara had been drifting in and out of the conversation. It was evening, and she was often very tired by the end of the day. Besides, she had been up early, had picked up her dress, had helped Rebecca with the flowers and had stood on her feet for several hours. Now, a drowsiness had set in, and she was leaning against Jake's thigh and hip, letting his sturdiness support her. His grey suit was slightly rough against her cheek, but she hadn't minded the feel of it. She was close enough to catch the pleasing scent of his cologne, and her mind had wandered to that morning when he had joined her in bed after his shower. They hadn't made love—there were times when Tamara felt too uncomfortable for that—but she had curled up in his arms as best she could, and they had lain there in a peaceful and soothing quiet, their thoughts their own, their bodies warm and comforting.

'What?' she asked.

'You two,' replied Cordelia. 'I've been wondering.'

'Wondering about what?' Tamara said.

'No wedding bells?' Henry asked.

'Wedding bells?' Tamara echoed in astonishment. 'Of course not.'

Henry blinked. 'I thought you were living together.'

Tamara shook her head. 'That doesn't mean marriage, Henry.'

'It's close,' he said. 'The next-best thing.'

'Jake and I have no intention of getting married,' Tamara declared firmly and looked up at Jake. 'Do we?'

Jake glanced down at her for a second, his expression unreadable, and then turned to the other two. 'We're just enjoying an illicit relationship,' he commented dryly, 'with no strings attached.'

'I see,' replied Henry, but Cordelia merely glanced at Jake with an odd look on her face that Tamara didn't understand at all.

There was no telling where the conversation might have gone on after that because the blare of music from the recreation room interrupted them, and Guy came over saying, 'The dancing has begun. The bride and groom have to start us off.'

'It doesn't sound like a waltz,' noted Henry worriedly, standing up.

'This is something modern, Henry,' Cordelia teased, 'Oil up your joints.'

Jake took hold of Tamara's hands and pulled her upright. 'Dance?'

'How do you dance with a pregnant lady?' she asked, standing up to him and swaying a bit. She often found herself slightly out of balance and having to hold on to someone or something.

'I don't know,' he said, instinctively supporting her with his arm, his eyes smiling down at her, 'but it looks like I'm going to find out.'

Later, when they were driving back to Jake's apartment after the festivities were over, Tamara said to him, 'Whoever gave Cordelia and Henry the idea that we were thinking of getting married?'

Jake shrugged. 'Weddings give people strange notions.'

'I couldn't believe it.'

'Why?'

'I thought we'd made it very clear.'

'Don't worry about it. Cordelia's always been after me to get married and settle down.'

It was a clear night and the pinpricks of stars could be seen through the window of the jeep. Tamara stared up into the blackness of the sky for a while and then at the passing landscape of suburban Calgary, house after house whizzing by, each with its own lit windows and private lives.

'Well,' she finally remarked, 'I'm hardly an eligible bride.'

Jake was silent for a moment, but when his voice came it was light and amused. 'You don't have to convince me.'

'I mean—we're basically incompatible over the long term. We don't even think alike.'

'Right.'

'And the baby isn't yours.'

'True.'

'And I'm going back to New York at the beginning of the summer.'

'So you say.'

Tamara frowned. 'It's the most ridiculous thing I've ever heard.'

'I wasn't about to propose.'

Still, the conversation niggled at her. Tamara couldn't fall asleep for thinking about it, and what annoyed her most was that she didn't have a clue why she even cared. It was very clear in her mind that she had no intention of marrying Jake or anybody for that matter and, from Jake's words, he didn't entertain any possibilities of marriage either. Oh, she had to concede that he was acting above and beyond the call of duty in taking care of a pregnant woman and even agreeing to be in the delivery room, but Tamara thought the agreement they had struck was fair and equitable. She gave Jake pleasure; she knew that. He enjoyed the way her mind worked and the spark of her conversation. They were perfect room-mates; she never worried about him or asked him where he had been when he was late, sensing that Jake wasn't a man who liked to have to account for every minute of his day. Even if she were in love with him, which she wasn't, of course, Tamara would never have been that possessive; she appreciated the value of independence far too much. And they were wonderful sex partners—despite all the impediments of her pregnancy.

But a permanent arrangement—that was out of the question. She had a life to lead that didn't include Jake or Calgary in it. In four months or so, she would be wiping the dust of the foothills off her feet and heading for the city that held her dream in its grasp. A feeling of nostalgia swept over her, a sweet remembering of the intensity and vividness of the life she had led in Manhattan. It was the sort of memory that ignored the squalid episodes and the dreariness of her apartment and concentrated on the excitement and thrill of being an actress, of being on the stage, of being in the thick of things. Tamara knew the pregnancy had changed her. She had felt the volume of her personality and temperament being tuned down by the alterations in her body; she had lost some of her sharp edges and the ferocity of her spirit, but she also believed that the changes were only temporary. The old Tamara would be restored once the baby was delivered, and she could return to New York, revived, invigorated and ready to conquer Broadway once again. The role of Medea hung before her, sparkling like a jewel in the future, its brilliance only just out of reach.

Which was why she couldn't understand her tossing and turning that night, her mind playing over and over again the interchange between Henry, Cordelia, Jake and herself. *Wedding bells. Of course not. An illicit relationship. No strings attached.* Of course, there were no strings attached. She didn't want to be tied to anyone, held down, anchored to some tidy domestic arrangement. Jake was admittedly wonderful; she quite . . . liked him. She was very fond of him. She thought the world of him. But marriage? Of course not. Out of the question. Absurd. So why couldn't she fall asleep when she was so tired, so very fatigued by the ponderous weight of her own body and the child that pressed heavily downward, awaiting the moment of its birth?

CHAPTER TEN

IT was to be their typical Friday lunch, but in honour of the occasion, Guy and Jake celebrated by having drinks at the top of the Husky Tower in a restaurant with a wide panoramic view of Calgary from its multi-sided windows. It was one of those days when the city seemed at its finest. The sky was clear, blue and stretched as far as the eye could see; in an easterly direction, it met the gold of the horizon in one smooth seam, to the west it joined in a jagged zipper with the pointed mountain peaks. A lone bird flew near the tower, swooping up and down with the prevailing winds, the black and white markings on its wings visible, its dark liquid eye taking them in as it flew past.

That morning Guy and Jake had received news of the largest contract in the history of their partnership, a million-dollar deal for a gas exploration project for Alberta Petroleum. They had spent a good part of the winter putting a proposal together, submitting it and then praying it would go through. Although they had done well with lesser jobs, they had both been aware that one of this magnitude put them in another category of business altogether. It meant hiring more men, expanding the office staff and buying extra equipment including a couple of bulldozers to clear brush. They had often sub-contracted that sort of work out before, but with this contract signed, sealed and ready to go, it meant they could afford to invest in their own machinery.

'I had a feeling it would go,' Guy was saying with quiet exultation as he sipped at a Scotch on the rocks. 'They'd been feeling me out about it for weeks in advance.'

'It was a good bid. We came in under Frazer and Associates.'

'They angled for too big a profit margin. They've been doing that lately. I guess that new office building is costing them more than they thought it would.'

Jake just nodded and picked up his drink, a Rusty Nail.

'We may have to move to another office ourselves.' Guy contemplated the prospect of a move with a smile of sheer pleasure. 'I'm not sure we'll have enough computer space when the data comes flowing in.'

'Yeah.'

'Just think of that data.' Guy stared out over the city with the expression of a conquerer. 'Not bad for two guys who came in with nothing but ideas.'

Jake lifted his drink. 'To ten years of partnership.'

Guy lifted his. 'To ten years,' he echoed happily and then drank. He put down his glass, about to bring forth another self-congratulatory pat on the back, when he finally noticed that Jake, despite the toast, didn't seem to share his enthusiasm. The other man was staring at the ice cubes in his Rusty Nail as if mesmerised, and there was a morose slump to his broad shoulders. Guy frowned at Jake's bent head and finally said, 'You don't seem happy about this.'

Jake looked up from his contemplation of his drink. 'Hey, I don't mean to give that impression. This is the best thing that's ever happened to us.'

'So why do I feel this is more of a wake than a celebration?'

Jake grimaced. 'Sorry about that.'

'What's up? It isn't the job, is it? Look, I know it's going to take a lot of work, but we can . . .'

'No, it isn't the job.'

'The jeep then—its transmission is acting up?'

A fleeting smile played over Jake's lips. 'No, the jeep is fine.'

'Then what the hell . . .' Guy stopped abruptly as a glimmer of understanding came home to him. 'It's Tamara, isn't it?'

Jake looked out over the vastness of Calgary and finally said. 'Yeah, it is.'

'The doctor didn't think there'd be any complications, did he?'

'No.'

'Well, then . . .'

'I wish to hell she'd never come here.' If Jake's voice had been angry, vehement or disgusted, Guy would not have been so alarmed. It was the quiet way the words were said, the flatness of the voice, that made Guy sit up.

'Look, if she's bugging you, send her back to

us. She wasn't supposed to end up living with you in the first place.'

'I said I'd be with her during the delivery.'

'What? During the delivery of the baby?'

'Yeah.'

'Jake, it isn't even your kid! I could barely make it through the birth of my own.'

Heavily. 'I said I would.'

'Why?'

'She's frightened and . . .' His smile was small and wry '. . . I'm a nice guy.'

Guy sat back in his chair and narrowed his eyes. 'I don't get it,' he said. 'The fact is, I haven't been able to figure this situation out at all. Jake, the perennial bachelor, gets himself hooked up with a woman who, to put it mildly, has been around the block a few times and is pregnant into the bargain.'

'I know it sounds weird.'

'Jake, it's the craziest thing I've ever heard of. Rebecca has her theories, of course, she always does, but I don't know what's got into you. Tamara isn't your type; she wasn't before, she isn't now and she's never going to be. I haven't said anything because I don't believe in interfering, but if she's making you miserable, then kick her out.'

Jake took another sip of his drink. 'I didn't know I had a type.'

Guy leaned forward. 'I've known you for twenty years, and I've never seen you get involved with a woman like this before. Look, don't get me wrong. I like Tamara, but she's different.

She's a big city girl; she's got big city dreams.'

'She says she's leaving when the baby is three months old.'

'There you are,' Guy said with satisfaction, 'she doesn't want to stay. So you'll be getting out of it soon enough.'

Jake wet his lips, tried to say something and then stopped.

'Rebecca's been all for this,' Guy went on. 'She thinks you two are made for one another, but I've told her to stop playing the matchmaker. Both of you are old enough to make up your own minds.'

The words finally came. 'Maybe I don't want to get out of it.'

'I also told her that, in my opinion, neither one of . . . what?'

'I said—maybe I don't want to get out of it.'

There was a long and awkward silence between them as the waiter came and took their order for lunch, filled their water glasses and removed their menus. The bird that had been circling the tower flew past the window again, slowed down and seemed to hang in the air for a moment as it contemplated Jake and Guy. Then, as if dismissing them, it fell quickly out of sight, its wings tucked close to its body for a long dive.

Guy cleared his throat. 'What do you mean?'

Jake gave him a rueful grin. 'I want to marry her.'

'Marry her?' The echo was faint, astonished, incredulous. 'God, Jake, you must be joking.'

'No.'

'Marry Tamara?'

'Yeah.'

'But she's . . . hell, she's pregnant, it isn't even your baby.'

'That doesn't seem to matter any more.'

'It doesn't?' Guy stared at Jake's face, saw the truth written across it and sat back, stunned. 'You're in love with her.'

'Unfortunately,' Jake answered dryly, 'that seems to be the case.'

'How, in God's name, did you ever get in that condition?'

Jake gave an unhappy shrug. There was no explaining the slow ascent from dislike to toleration to appreciation to love. He didn't understand it himself, and he knew how bizarre it was to fall in love with a pregnant woman in the first place. But somehow the pregnancy hadn't seemed to make any difference; he had found Tamara so desirable that the bulging curve of her belly hadn't dimmed her attraction for him at all. In fact, he had been struck one day by how pleasing her nude, pregnant body actually was. She had been standing by the closet, reaching upwards for a sweater, a pink-pointed breast lifted, her abdomen arched and traced with a delicate filigree of blue veins, her legs slim and seemingly too fragile to bear the weight above. A lump had inexplicably grown in his throat, and his urge had been to pull her into his arms, to hold her close to him, to start that slow, warm dance until their bodies were joined. That was the only way that Jake knew to express his feelings for Tamara. In that respect, he was like most men; the emotion of love and his need for sex were so intertwined in his thinking that he could not tell where one began and the other left off.

Guy was shaking his head in disbelief. 'You've spent most of your adult life avoiding commitment to perfectly nice, ordinary women who would have been only too happy to supply you with your own family, and now you've fallen for someone like Tamara.'

'Maybe that was it,' Jake acknowledged. 'Those ordinary women were boring. If there's one thing you can say about Tam, it's that she's interesting.'

'To say the least,' agreed Guy dryly.

Their salads arrived and a basket of rolls. Jake took one and buttered it, saying as he did so, 'I don't want to be in love with her. Don't think I haven't fought it. And she isn't the least bit interested in marrying me. She has her sights set on going back to New York.'

Guy reached for a roll of his own. 'Does she know how you feel?'

'No, I haven't had the . . . nerve to tell her. I'm not fond of rejection. I've been leading a goddamned double life, keeping up the façade that our relationship is strictly a one-shot deal while wanting . . . wishing . . .' Jake ground his teeth together with an audible sound. 'Oh, hell!'

Guy's glance was sympathetic. 'The bigger they are, the harder they fall.'

'Yeah,' Jake muttered, 'something like that.'

'Look, maybe she wouldn't reject you after all.

Maybe she's hankering after the same thing.'

Jake shook his head. 'Not a chance. She's all keen to go back; there's a role she wants to try out for.'

'It isn't going to be easy being an actress and a single mother without any money.'

'I've tried to tell her that.'

Guy gave him a look of sympathy. 'Tam isn't the sort to listen to anything she doesn't want to hear.'

Jake scowled into his salad. 'I know.'

Suddenly Guy was grinning. 'Rebecca isn't going to believe this,' he said.

Jake's head shot up. 'Don't tell her!'

'No? She'll plead your case, she'll be your best advocate.'

'I have to talk to Tam on my own.'

'When are you going to do that?'

'I don't know,' Jake answered and then repeated the words, slowly, 'I don't know.'

Several days later, Tamara was blocking the sweater she had knitted for Jake when Rebecca arrived at the apartment. The sweater was a pullover made of a royal blue yarn and had cables in the front and on the sleeves. It had been her most ambitious project to date, and she was quite pleased with it. She dipped the sections; the front, back and sleeves, in cold water, wrung them out gently and laid them on towels. When they were dry she would sew up the seams and knit the neckline. She was humming to herself as she worked, imagining Jake in the sweater and thinking how well he would look in blue with his blond hair and fair colouring.

Tamara was happy this morning. Since happiness wasn't a state of mind that she found herself in very often, she enjoyed the sensation while she could. Part of it came, she knew, from an unusually good night's sleep, a very slow lovemaking session that morning—how many women had wonderful sex when they were so very pregnant?—and from a spray of roses that had come by delivery just before lunch, tender pink buds of roses lying on a bed of delicate green ferns. There had been a note tucked in among the roses with Jake's name written in his strong script. The fact that there wasn't a message hadn't bothered Tamara. The glow of the morning had been strong enough to stay with both of them; Jake was remembering it with flowers, Tamara by the feel of his sweater between her fingers.

Life seemed so pleasant to her for a change that when the bell rang, she was smiling when she opened the door and Rebecca said. 'You look happy.'

'Jake's sweater is going to be beautiful, if I have to say so myself.'

Rebecca stepped inside and plunked down the baby car-bed she had been carrying. It was piled high with baby clothes, little plastic toys and a pink plastic baby bath. 'Here's what I dug out for you. It isn't much for starters, but it should serve for a month or two.'

'I won't need a crib for a while, will I?'

'No.'

As Rebecca took off her coat, Tamara lifted out each item of baby clothing and turned it over in her hand. There were doll-size stretch sleepers in pastel colours with snaps up the front, terry-towelling bibs with sayings on them like 'I Love Grandma', infinitesimal white undershirts that criss-crossed in front with narrow ribbon ties, rubber pants, booties, and a bunting bag with a miniature alphabet embroidered across the front. 'They're so tiny,' she sighed.

'You won't believe how fast the baby will out-grow them. Jennifer was out of this stuff within two months.'

'I saw the doctor yesterday,' Tamara announced, 'and he was in the mood for predic-tion. He said the baby should be around eight pounds, and it's dropped. Not that he had to tell me that. Honestly, Becks, I feel as if I'm going to give birth from my kneecaps.'

Rebecca smiled. 'That would be a novelty. You'd make medical history.'

Tamara led the way into Jake's narrow kitchen. 'Coffee?' she asked. 'Tea?'

'A quick tea,' Rebecca answered, perching on a stool. 'I can't stay long. The kids are with a neighbour who has a dentist appointment in half an hour.'

'You look tired.'

Rebecca brushed her long auburn hair back and sighed. 'Jennifer's getting molars and was up during the night. Why did God make teething so difficult?'

'To torture mothers.'

'Just wait, Tam, until it's your turn.'

Tamara plugged in the electric kettle. 'I can't wait. I've had it with being pregnant.'

Rebecca watched her sister bustle around the kitchen. Tamara was wearing a pair of black maternity slacks and a pale green top; her hair had grown several inches since her arrival in Calgary and now fell below her shoulders in a curly mass. She had pulled it carelessly back with a green ribbon so that strands of it curled at her temples and on her forehead. 'Actually,' Rebecca finally replied, 'it becomes you.'

'What? Being pregnant?'

'Mmmmm—you were too angular before. Your face has filled out a bit.'

'I'm going to have to go on a diet when this is over. I've gained thirty pounds.'

Rebecca ignored her. 'On the other hand, maybe it isn't the pregnancy.'

The cheerful light in Tamara's world was waning. She turned slowly. 'Okay, Becks,' she said in a warning tone, 'I know you're about to say something meaningful and insightful. You've got that tone of voice.'

Rebecca was used to Tamara's sarcasm. 'Perhaps, it's Jake.'

'Ah-ah. I knew you couldn't resist it.'

'A little love goes a long way, doesn't it?'

'For God's sake, Becks, don't be so slushy and sentimental. It's disgusting. And besides, we're friends. How many times do I have to tell you that?'

'Friends? Come on, Tam. That's a myth you've been holding on to for months. Why not admit what's really going on?'

Tamara set two cups on the counter with a small slam. 'Why should I?' she returned sulkily.

'You're going to do it for me.'

'As your older sister . . .'

'God!'

'And as someone who understands these things far better than you do . . .'

'You can't be serious.'

'And who has been acquainted with Jake for five years compared to your two months.'

'The only truthful thing you've said yet.'

'He's in love with you.'

Tamara glared at her. 'Don't be ridiculous!'

Rebecca smiled at her with satisfaction. 'Now, why does that make you so angry?'

'Because it isn't true, because you want to believe it so badly that you're making up stories, because you don't understand the relationship between Jake and myself, because . . .'

'Because you want to avoid the truth.'

'Rebecca, you're a disgusting romantic.'

'Tam, I know Jake. Except for sex, he's always avoided women. Oh, he's had his affairs, hundreds of them, in fact, but they've all been casual. I've always thought that underneath that carefree bachelor façade is a man who is basically afraid of women—something to do with his mother, I suppose. But he's different with you. He's given up his privacy and independence and let you move in.'

'That's because my being here is only temporary.'

Rebecca gave her a long look. 'Is it?'

'Of course. I'm going back to New York, I told you that already. There's a play there that I'll be auditioning for.'

'You're crazy, you know.'

'Becks, I'm an actress.'

'And you'll be a mother.'

'The two can exist in the same time-frame.'

'Not easily. Tam, you're living in a dream world. Babies take a lot of effort and love.'

'The world is full of single mothers who work and bring up children.'

'I know, but it's hard, particularly when you'll have so little money.'

Tamara's state of happiness had now vanished completely. In a frosty voice, she said, 'I'll manage.'

The kettle had started to boil then and its whistle was shrill. Tamara put two tea-bags in the teapot and poured the boiling water over them. Her actions masked the tension in the air. The sisters rarely fought or, to put it more precisely, Rebecca rarely attempted a head-long confrontation with Tamara. An attack like that had always struck her as foolish and dangerous. Tamara was a fighter and her ire was raised easily; when they were children, Rebecca had discovered that the best way to handle her sister had been through indirect manipulation. But the impending birth had brought Rebecca to the point that she was willing to do battle. The thought of Tamara struggling with a baby in New York while Jake mourned in Calgary had made her desperate.

'You won't manage,' she now said, her own voice cool. 'You'll end up on Martine's doorstep, begging for hand-outs.'

Tamara swerved around, lost her balance and had to grab a counter's edge to steady herself. 'The hell I will!'

'Want to bet on it?'

'I wouldn't go near Martine with a ten-foot pole.'

'Beggars can't be choosers—you'll be living from hand to mouth.'

'I know how to live on a tight budget. I've done it for years.'

'You have no idea what it's going to be like.'

Tamara's eyes glinted with anger and her colour was high. 'So what are you suggesting? That I stay in Calgary and marry a man for a meal-ticket?'

'No.'

'That's what it sounds like to me.'

'What I'm suggesting, Tam,' and here Rebecca softened her voice, 'is that you face reality. You have a baby coming, you're living with a man who loves you . . . oh, yes, he does, I don't care what you think . . . and it's quite possible that underneath all your protests to the contrary, that you . . . love him in return.'

Tamara stared at her sister, her face expressing at the same time the emotions of disbelief, disdain and incredulity. Then the actress in her came to the fore, and she tossed her head, put her hands on her hips and looked skywards as if searching out the gods. 'The woman is insane,' she said in a dramatic voice. 'Stark, raving mad.'

Rebecca ignored the theatrics. 'You've never even liked a man before. There must be something about Jake that pleases you.'

In her anger, Tamara aimed for a lethal blow to this argument, one that would cut it off with one clean slice. 'He is,' she said in clear, concise words, 'a good f—'

Rebecca didn't even blink. 'I don't ever really think you liked sex before.'

'Don't play the heavy psychiatrist with me.'

'Tam, why not admit that there's more to your relationship with Jake than lies on the surface? You're happy with him—start with that.'

'I am not the type to be interested in domestic bliss.'

'Then you're giving a fine imitation of someone who is.'

Tamara leaned forward to make her point. 'I'm playing at it,' she said. 'It's like a role in a production. I could drop it tomorrow and not miss it at all.'

'I don't believe that.'

Tamara's voice was rising with frustration. 'I'm not like you, don't you understand that?'

'You're a woman who needs love and affection,' Rebecca replied calmly, 'just like the rest of us.'

'No, damn it! I don't intend to give up my independence for Jake, no matter how much you want me to. He's still a country boy who lives in the boondocks as far as I'm concerned—and a cultural illiterate with the taste-buds of a peasant!'

Rebecca glanced at the spray of roses in the vase by the sink. 'And he sends you flowers, is good in bed and is even going to stay with you in the delivery room. I think he's a jewel, Tam, a rare and unusual gem of a man. He's too valuable to toss away for a veneer of sophistication and a knowledge of French cuisine.'

Tamara tried to stare her sister down. 'Maybe he doesn't want me—has that occurred to you?'

Rebecca stared right back. 'Why don't you ask him and find out?'

'Maybe I will,' Tamara declared through clenched teeth. 'Anything to get you off my case.'

Rebecca felt the faint taste of victory and smiled. 'I like being on your case,' she confessed. 'It feels like old times.'

Tamara took a deep breath. 'You're a pain, Becks, a goddamned persistent pain. You always were.'

'So you'll ask him?'

'Nag, nag.'

'Nagging comes with the territory of motherhood,' answered Rebecca serenely. 'Wait and see.'

Of course, Tamara had no intention of asking Jake anything. It was quite clear in her mind what the parameters of their relationship were. The rules had been established earlier and neither of them had deviated from these carefully laid down expectations. Easy, free and open—that's the way they both wanted it and that's the way it had remained. The flowers, the good sex, and Jake's presence when the baby was born didn't change their unspoken pact. Tamara realised that Rebecca couldn't really understand what made their affair work. Her sister came to their relationship with the perspective of a happily married woman. She thought the lack of friction between Jake and Tamara was a result of love. She couldn't, not in a million years, conceive of the fact that their compatibility was really underlain by indifference.

Yes, Tamara thought with a trace of smugness, indifference—that was it. What else could account for the lack of possessiveness? The small courtesies that made their living together so smooth a meshing? Tamara was far too wise in the ways of men to be lulled into any dream that she and Jake were a match made in marital heaven. She knew all about passion, about jealousy, about the large and small ways in which lovers can wound one another. She had been through it so many times that she could have outlined the stages of the penultimate love affair. First, there was the sparking of interest, the seductive games, the passion, either real or false depending on the players, the inevitable setting in of disillusion, the tacky battles, the vicious name-calling. It always boiled down to the same thing in the end—when passion died there was nothing left but dislike.

But she and Jake had started an affair on an entirely different premiss. They had been forced into domestic roles when Rebecca and Guy had gone to Mexico and the children had caught chicken-pox. Their initial dislike of one another had eased into acceptance and, both being adults, they had sought out the one thing from one another that could make this acceptance more comfortable. Sex had merely been a friendly gesture that catered to both their needs. They had liked it enough to want to continue a good thing, and her moving in with Jake had been a matter of convenience. The arrangement was odd by most people's standards, but what made it work was an essential *uncaring* at its basis. They were kind to one another, it was true, but those entangling and violent emotions of passion and love were missing.

Tamara was, frankly, much happier that way. She didn't have to worry about what Jake was thinking or doing every minute; she didn't have to care if she looked like hell one day or was out of sorts on another. As far as affairs went, it was certainly one of the nicest she had ever been in, but to suggest that Jake loved her and she loved him—well, that was pure, unadulterated hogwash dreamt up in Rebecca's feverish, romantic imagination. And to suggest that she give up Manhattan, the role of Medea and her old life for a peaceful, quiet marriage was ludicrous. Hormones might be taming her down for the duration of her pregnancy, but Tamara knew what she would be like after the baby was born.

She would crave the excitement then, the sounds and noises of New York, the gossip, the stores, the theatre, the resurgence of ambition, the dream of bringing the city to its knees. Calgary wouldn't be able to hold her then; she would be beating her wings against its provincialism like a bird trapped in a confining cage.

So Tamara went blithely on her way, ignoring everything around her but the things she wanted to see. She and Jake went shopping on Saturday morning for groceries, she tried on some nursing bras at a maternity store, then they came back and made lunch together. If Jake gave her an odd glance now and then she didn't notice it, nor did she catch a look on his face that expressed a baffled frustration. She chattered on about the sweater she was making, the clothes Rebecca had brought for the baby, the doctor's last statement regarding the baby's potential weight and the fact that she still couldn't settle down on any names.

After lunch, she went with him to the squash club since she had agreed to be part of his cheering squad during the last tournament on the ladder. Tamara had never seen a game of squash played before so she was quite surprised by the swiftness of it and the aggression of the players. The ball whizzed through the air like a bullet, slamming against walls, while Jake and his opponent jockeyed for position.

'DeBlais is out for the kill,' some man said behind her.

'He's a mean and tricky competitor,' another said.

Tamara turned back to the game, a frown marring the smooth skin between her eyebrows as she watched Jake play, his shoulders straining against the white of his shirt, muscles bulging in his arms and legs, his headband dark with sweat. He had always seemed to her to be gentle and sometimes awkward in the endearing, clumsy way of very large men. She had never seen him as being agile, devious and mean; she had never really thought of Jake as an aggressive fighter, as a man who would go in for the kill. The squash match was something of a revelation to Tamara as was Jake's grin in her direction after it was over, the triumphal gesture he made with his hand towards the rest of the audience, and her realisation that Jake was the kind of man who liked to win. For a moment, he had seemed like a perfect stranger.

The feeling of estrangement returned and deepened later that evening when the phone rang and Tamara picked it up. 'Hello?' she said.

There was a pause as if her voice was unexpected and then a woman's voice, fraught with tension and tears, asked, 'Is Jake there?'

Tamara raised an eyebrow and turned to Jake. 'For you,' she told him. It wasn't the first time a woman had called the apartment, but never had a caller sounded so desperate.

'Carla,' Jake said. 'How are you? . . . What? When? . . . Are you all right . . . ?'

There was a long silence on Jake's part while Tamara glanced at him and then away. She didn't want to seem overly nosy in what was obviously a conversation between Jake and a former lover.

'When did he go?' Jake went on. '. . . Are you afraid he'll come . . . Take it easy . . . easy now . . . Carla, honey . . . no, of course I don't mind. I must have the widest shoulder in Calgary . . . Tonight? Well, I . . .' Jake glanced over at Tamara who gave a nonchalant shrug. Jake frowned for a second and then turned his attention back to the phone. 'Sure, I don't mind . . . no, you're not interrupting anything. Give me about twenty minutes . . . Right, now, hold on and don't do anything desperate.'

Even Tamara could hear from the sounds emanating from the receiver that Carla was sobbing in relief. So when Jake hung up the phone, she merely said, 'An old girl-friend got herself in trouble?'

'Her husband beat her up and then walked out.'

'So it's Jake to the rescue.'

He had walked to the closet and was reaching for a jacket, but now he turned around. 'Do you mind? She's afraid he'll come back.'

Tamara drew herself up as tall as possible, an almost impossible feat when eight pounds of foetus seemed to be dragging her to the ground. 'Me? Of course not.'

His voice was flat. 'I didn't think so.'

She lifted her hands in a gesture of surrender. 'No holds,' she reminded him.

He shrugged on the jacket. 'I may be late. Don't wait up.'

'Fine,' she replied and then he was out the door.

It was with a sense of smugness that Tamara closed the door behind him. See, she felt like saying to Rebecca. See how wrong you were—an old mistress can phone, Jake immediately answers the call of duty and Tamara lets him go without a pang. There was nothing to it. See?

She went into the living room, picked up Jake's sweater and resumed sewing the side seams, but she grew restless after a while and turned on the television. Tamara watched, without seeing, two sitcoms and a variety show. Then she turned the television off and walked into the kitchen—waddled, actually. She had reached that stage of pregnancy where forward locomotion involved a swaying from side to side that no longer resembled anything human. As she opened the door of the refrigerator and stared at the pitcher of orange juice, the plate of cold hamburgers and the leftovers of cole-slaw, the thought came unbidden to her mind—he's tired of me, he wants a woman whose waistline is slim, one who walks with grace and charm.

Tamara slammed the refrigerator door, knocking off two magnetfuls of paper. She cursed out loud and, with difficulty, squatted down and picked up the scattered notes she and Jake had jotted down for one another. Then she clicked off the light in the kitchen and went into the bedroom where she undressed and pulled on a sleeveless cotton nightgown that billowed out over the globe of her stomach like a curtain blowing in the wind. For the first time in her pregnancy, she positively hated the way she looked —she was a blimp, an elephant, a grotesquely swollen caricature of a woman. Her belly-button stuck out like an oversized thimble, it itched like the dickens, and the veins in her legs had become prominent under the strain of circulation. They looked like two road-maps of Europe. Only her breasts withstood the harshness of her scrutiny; they were full and round and sexy. The areolae had darkened almost to a red, the nipples were large enough to satisfy even the most ravenous infant.

Tamara slipped into bed and tried to read a mystery novel. When that didn't work, she turned off the light and tried to sleep. That was her biggest mistake of the evening. The very first image that came into her mind was of Jake in bed soothing the weeping and oh-so-soothable Carla. He was a physical man, the type who used his hands and body to express his emotions and his sympathy. Tamara knew that; she had been at the receiving end often enough herself. It shocked her, however, to realise that she didn't want any other woman to be in the same position. Where was all of her vaunted indifference? Her lack of possessiveness? Her easy-come, easy-go attitude?

Tamara sat up in bed, snapped the light back on and stared at Jake's empty pillow. Don't wait up, he had said. The implication had been obvious, hadn't it? And she wasn't supposed to care. The horrible part was that she had discovered that she did care, that over the three months she had lived with Jake, slept with him and shared his life, something other than casual friendship had stolen in unawares, entwining itself through her, tugging at her and causing a new sort of pain in her chest. Tamara didn't know precisely what it was, but she didn't like it. She didn't want to give a damn if Jake were the consolation prize for half a dozen unhappy women. She wanted to be able to contemplate the possibility of his kissing and caressing another woman without her heart skipping a beat and her breath feeling laboured and her hands trembling.

She wanted to—but, goddamn it, she couldn't.

CHAPTER ELEVEN

JAKE put his hand on the knob of his apartment door and gave a sigh that combined fatigue and frustration. Carla had been half-hysterical by the time he arrived at her house and he had spent the next hour calming her down and finally convincing her to call the police. He had left her in the hands of a woman police sergeant who was sympathetic and savvy about domestic violence. With the question of Carla's safety out of the way, he had then been able to concentrate on that final scene with Tamara.

Not that he wanted to—he wanted to forget her careless indifference, her shrug of nonchalance and that small and telling statement. No holds, she had said. No holds, no knots, no ties, no commitment—that's what she had meant, and it made Jake grind his teeth and clench his hands on the steering-wheel with an impotent anger. Ever since his confession to Guy, his situation with Tamara had seemed to grow more and more futile. He wished to hell he hadn't fallen in love with her, but nothing could take away an emotion that had developed without his being aware of it. In the barren ground of his soul, it had taken root and, without encouragement or nurturing, it had flourished and wound its way into his heart. If he could, he would have torn it out with his bare hands, but love isn't an overgrown bush or a vine weaving its way into the cracks of a building. It's an ephemeral, subtle thing, as insubstantial as a fleeting shadow, as the blink of an eye, as a scent caught in a breeze. Yet, once enthroned, it cannot be dislodged or moved or altered.

Jake had never felt anything like it. His love for Tamara hurt more than any pain he had ever felt before. He had to watch her, to talk to her and to make love to her without uttering the sentiment that trembled on his lips. He had been afraid of the scorn that would shower over his head if he told her that he loved her; Jake could just imagine the derisive curl of her lip, the hoot of laughter, the ridicule in her eyes. He didn't dare expose himself to that sort of rejection so he said nothing and, in his inarticulate manner, tried to express himself in other ways. His kisses were more passionate, his touch increasingly gentle. He had even once sent her roses. But, in this case, actions did not speak louder than words. Tamara never seemed to notice the small gestures by which Jake offered to her his mute and fragile love.

He had been prepared to enter the apartment quietly in the expectation that Tamara would be asleep but instead, when he pushed open the door, he discovered that every light was blazing. He stood in the foyer and then heard the sounds. A voice issued from the living room, a voice that was powerful and feminine and only barely discernible as belonging to Tamara. Jake silently shut the door behind him, stepped forward and

then blinked. She was standing in profile to him
and would have hardly been recognisable if it
hadn't been for the blazing orange of her hair and
the protuberance of her belly.

She wore a long, black gown and half a dozen
chains and strands of multi-coloured beads.
Huge gold hoops swung from her ears. She had
made her face up into a mask; her lids accentu-
ated by a deep shading of blue and purple
shadow, her eyes outlined in black. The freckles
on her nose and cheeks were covered with
powder. Her lips were scarlet. Her hair had been
brushed outwards so that it flamed around her
face, an unholy halo. She was reading from a
book that she held in one hand, and he saw that
her nails had been painted a red to match the
colour of her lips.

'Still more, a foreign woman, coming among
   new laws,
New customs, needs the skill of magic, to find
   out
What her home could not teach her, how to
   treat the man
Whose bed she shares. And if in this exacting
   toil
We are successful, and our husband does not
   struggle
Under the marriage yoke, our life is enviable.
Otherwise, death is better. If a man grows tired
Of the company at home, he can go out, and
   find . . .'

Jake cleared his throat and Tamara turned slowly. Beneath the heavy, glittering and colourful lids of her eyes, she glared at him, and he could only stare back at her, his mouth dry, stunned by that imperious, sapphire glance set in its cold, exotic mask. The pregnancy that strained at the black cloth didn't take away from the olympian anger that emanated from her, and the knowledge that he had possessed her a hundred times didn't soften Jake's sense of shock. Ill-will, malice and hatred seemed to hover in the air between them, an almost visible, electric arc of animosity.

'Tamara?' he finally ventured to say.

'Medea,' she snapped and, throwing the book down to the floor, completed the passage;

'A cure for tediousness. We wives are forced to look
To one man only. And, they tell us, we at home
Live free from danger, they go out to battle: fools!
I'd rather stand three times in the front line than bear
One child.'

'You're rehearsing for your audition tonight?' he asked in astonishment.

'Is there a better time?'

'It's almost one o'clock in the morning.'

Tamara walked regally over to the window and stared out into the expanse of night sky, her profile haughty against the curtains, her fingers

clenched into blood-red claws at her sides. 'I
didn't really expect you to come home,' she said.

Jake realised his mouth was hanging open and
he shut it quickly. 'You didn't?'

Her hand waved negligently in the air. 'Didn't
Carla require your presence?'

Something was puzzling Jake, but he couldn't
put his finger on it. 'I called the police.'

The blue eyes widened a fraction. 'Oh,' she
replied.

Jake gave her a surprised look. 'What else did
you think I was going to do?'

'Nothing.'

A pause and then, 'You thought I was going to
go to bed with her?'

Tamara shrugged. 'You're free to do as you
please.'

The suspicion had been growing inside of Jake
ever since he had walked through the front door
and found Tamara enacting the part of Medea,
but now the confirmation of that suspicion
clicked firmly into place. *If a man grows tired/
Of the company at home, he can go out and find . . .*
That's what she had been saying when he had
returned, speaking that angry soliloquy and glar-
ing at him as if he had been Jason, as if he had left
her for another woman. She had lifted her chin in
a regal fashion and turned then to watch the dim,
white moon hover in the black sky, her face as
blank of expression as that of the moon's faraway
visage. Twenty-four hours ago, Jake would have
been at a loss to explain Tamara's odd behaviour.
From the day he had first met her, she had

seemed mysterious and unpredictable to him, an exotically scented wild flower tossing its head among the orderly rows of marigolds and primroses. But now he suddenly understood her. A jolt of his heart made him move, and Jake stepped forward, not realising that he was holding his breath until he was standing right behind her, looking down into that incredible mass of orange curls.

'You're jealous,' he remarked.

Tamara whirled around, not an easy accomplishment considering her displaced centre of gravity. 'What?'

'Wasn't that Medea's problem?' Jake went on. 'She was insanely jealous.'

'What would I be jealous of?'

'Of Carla. Of the way I went to help her.'

The mask looked disgusted. 'If you think I give a damn about your old girl-friends then I . . .'

Belief gave him confidence, and confidence gave him the strength to voice what had seemed impossible before. 'No,' he continued quietly, 'I think that you give a damn about me.'

For a second the mast wavered and then held firm. The glittering, angry eyes looked him up and down and then Tamara began to laugh. It was a laugh of disbelief, astonishment and hilarity. It was also an artificial stagy laugh that made Jake's teeth grit together. It went on and on, filling the room with its awful sound, until he could stand it no longer. He grabbed Tamara by the shoulders and shook her.

'Stop it!' he yelled.

She laughed some more.

'God damn it! Stop it!'

He was shaking her, violently now. Jake wasn't a man given to rage, but Tamara had always been capable of bringing out emotions in him that never seemed to have existed before. The anger held elements of his old irritation with her, but it was also bound up with humiliation, frustration and love, the latter giving it a force and breadth beyond anything Jake had ever experienced before. It raged through his body, a wild and ravening beast, it blurred his vision, its pounding filled his ears like the sounds of waves crashing against stone. He shook her until her head wobbled, but he couldn't stop. He was terrified that if he let go of her shoulders, he would then strangle her with his bare hands.

It was a while before Jake realised that the sounds had changed and that what was coming out of Tamara's mouth was no longer laughter. She was crying, and the sapphire eyes were swimming with tears. Appalled at what he had done, Jake stopped, dropped his hands to his sides and clenched them into fists, pressing them against his body so that they could not commit any further act of atrocity.

He took a deep and shaky breath. 'I'm sorry,' he apologised, 'but I can't stand it any longer. We're living a ridiculous charade. At least, I know it, even if you don't. I'm tired of the lying—the emotional lying, that is. The way you could let me go out the door tonight, acting as if it didn't matter, when underneath you really cared.'

Even though there were tears running down her cheeks, Tamara was defiant. 'I didn't.'

The fists rose, but Jake slammed one of them into the other. It was preferable to inflict violence on himself than to hurt Tamara. 'Why can't you admit it? Because you're too proud?'

'I don't know what you're talking about.'

'The hell you don't.' But he saw from the set of her mouth that she wasn't going to yield that easily and his voice was bitter. 'All right, if you won't talk then I will. I'll tell you what it's like to wake up next to you every morning, come home to you at night, make love to you, eat dinner with you, go out with you and try to act as if we're nothing more than friends. It's insane—it's driving me crazy, because I don't feel that way about you. Oh, I did in the beginning, but I don't any more. For some crazy reason, I fell in love with you.' He held up a hand when she tried to speak. 'I know what you think. We're mismatched, you wouldn't spend another moment in Calgary if you had to, you hate the domestic scene, you despise Rebecca for being happy. I've heard it all, a thousand times, but I don't want to hear it any more. I can't stand it. Do you understand? I can't stand it!'

Her lips were stiff as if she was trying to stop them from trembling. 'You . . . can't love me.'

'Why not? Do you think I'm incapable of loving anyone?' She didn't speak but stared at him as if horrified, and Jake roughly ran his fingers through his hair, tossing its golden strands. 'All right, I've never loved a woman before, I admit that. I know the effect my mother had on me. She left when I was two and my father always told me I was the reason. That's why your pregnancy made me so angry when I first knew you. Having children should be a privilege, not the result of some accidental meeting of bodies. A child needs its parents, it needs a father and a . . . mother.'

To his horror, Jake felt his voice crack. He almost gave up at that point, but the impetus of his emotions was too strong to be stopped and, swallowing, he kept on, his voice growing steady again. 'Anyway, I've always been afraid of women who weren't predictable. I chose women who would follow my pattern for an affair without causing trouble. I was a bastard. I admit that, but I couldn't have handled it any other way. My mother wasn't predictable, you see. She was different; she left my father and she abandoned me. It wasn't until I met you that I could face being with a woman who wasn't like the others, who didn't act the way other women did, who had a mind of her own. Not that I wanted to fall in love with you. Don't think I did. The fact is, I hated the thought of it and fought it every chance I could.'

'I . . . don't want you to love me.'

'You're afraid of it, aren't you?'

She flung her head back, and he could see that she had recovered some of her poise. 'It would ruin everything. What we have is . . . is very nice. It's not exhausting or agonising. It's . . . pleasant.'

'Pleasant!' Jake could have crushed the word

beneath the heel of his boot. 'Is that all you want from a man, something . . . pleasant?'

The mask had slipped back on. 'I'm pregnant. I'm going to have a baby and I don't need to be involved in anything upsetting.'

Jake ignored her. 'Why can't you admit you love me?'

'Love you! I don't, that's why.'

'You do.'

'Don't be ridiculous!'

That statement might have crushed an earlier Jake, but it had no effect on him now. Certainty had grown within him through every angry exchange of words. The mask she had applied was only superficial after all; he was sure he could see the truth in her eyes. 'Then why were you so angry when I went to Carla?'

The glittering, coloured lids dropped dramatically down over her eyes for a second as if Tamara were seeking an internal strength and then lifted again. 'I wasn't angry.'

'No? Then what's all this crap about Medea.'

'I was practising. I intend to get the role.'

Jake spun on his heel, walked over to the couch, sat down on it and smiled lethally at her. 'All right, let's talk about your career.'

Tamara was still for a second and then, giving him a wary glance, walked over and sat down in the chair opposite him. 'What about my career?'

'Let's talk about why you're such a failure.'

Jake had known the words would cut, but he hadn't anticipated the way she straightened up, the way the offence made her square her narrow shoulders, the turning down of that scarlet mouth into an angry grimace, the putting together of her palms so that the long nails were aimed at him like ten small, dark-red knives.

'I'm not a failure.' The words came out, each one separate and distinct from its neighbour.

'You are. You are a failed actress. You never got a big role in your life, and you've spent most of your time scrambling around for little ones. Your chances of getting Medea are infinitesimal.'

'Your ignorance appals me. You know nothing about theatre.'

'I don't have to know anything about theatre to know why you haven't been a success. It's obvious to anyone who thinks about it.'

'Really—and now you're going to pretend to be a critic.'

Jake ignored her. 'It has to come from inside, Tamara. Acting isn't a superficial thing like putting on make-up and jewellery and odd clothes. It's what's in the heart that counts and you haven't had anything in yours except hatred for your parents. You've been empty, shallow, you've never had any real emotion to fall back on except anger.' Tamara's throat was working; he could see the tendons move convulsively. 'Oh, I'll admit that you had a dramatic flair and a colourful personality, but I'm sure that wasn't enough. You're fighting yourself all the time. Any feeling that comes your way is squashed out of existence. Hell, you can't even admit to yourself that you're jealous and that you love me.'

The words rushed out of her in angry tumult. 'I don't love you. I hate you.'

'No, I don't believe that.'

Her small jaws were clenched. 'I've never loved any man.'

'Why?'

'I just haven't.'

'I know why I've never fallen in love before,' Jake said, 'and it took a hell of a lot of soul-searching to find out. It wasn't easy, but I did it.'

'I don't have to search my soul.'

But her eyes were wide with fear, and Jake felt the triumph of someone who is close to achieving his goal. Relentlessly, he pressed on. 'Why not? You think you're normal? Bed-hopping, sleeping with so many men that you can't figure out which one impregnated you? Being so angry at men that you've never been able to form a decent relationship with one?'

'Leave me alone!' She stood up and he saw that she was trembling.

'And when you finally do, you can't admit it?'

'*Leave me alone!*'

Tamara started to run, but she was so heavy with child that she merely waddled faster. She grabbed at things as she went, the edge of a table, a vase that fell and crashed to the ground, a chair that scraped the floor as she pushed it aside. The determination to rid herself of him was written in every motion, but her physical inability to do what she wanted with grace and finesse made Jake's heart rise to his throat in a lump. She was

awkward, unwieldy; there was a sad poignancy
to her helplessness and vulnerability. He wanted
to protect her from indignity, but she had
brought this on herself, on both of them.

Tamara lurched slightly, and he realised that
she must be crying again. Her back was to him;
one hand groped ahead of her while the other
flailed to one side as if she anticipated running
into a wall. When her hip collided with a table,
she flinched and he came to life.

Within a stride, he was beside her, his arms
going around her shoulders. 'Tam, it can't be that
bad. If you'd just get it out of your system so it
will stop poisoning . . .'

She flung his arm off and turned to face him.
He was shocked by the change in her. All the
haughty insolence was gone, and in its place was
a look of pure anguish. Her eyes were wet and
she was breathing hard, her chest moving in a
furious tempo. 'LEAVE ME ALONE!'

Jake refused to be frightened by her scream, by
her fist slamming into his chest, by the panic he
saw in her eyes. 'No,' he argued firmly, grabbing
her wrist. 'You have to tell me.'

'*No!*'

'Yes.' She was shaking so hard that the tips of
her hair trembled. Her face had gone pale
beneath its dusting of powder, and her eyes
were blue pools surrounded by smudges of
mascara. He pulled her as close to him as her
pregnancy allowed and said, 'I love you and I
love your baby. I can't offer you any more than
that, but you'll have to be honest with me. For

once in your life, you're going to have to tell the truth.'

Her mouth moved, echoing his words. *The Truth*.

'The truth,' he continued firmly. 'Plain and simple. No drama, no histrionics, no acting. Do you understand?'

Her voice was such a low whisper that he had to bend to hear it. 'I can't.'

'Yes, you can. You're going to do it right now.' His arms tightened around her so that when the baby began to move both of them could feel it kicking between them. 'Right now.'

It had been an ordinary day. She had gone to school and come home in the afternoon just in time to take Celia out in her carriage. She was nine years old and Celia was just a baby—she hadn't even had her first birthday yet. Tamara thought she was the world's cutest baby. She had coppery curls all around her head, wide blue eyes and a chin with a dimple in it. She liked to walk her sister because then she could imagine that Celia was her baby and that she was the mother of the house and that soon her husband, a faceless masculine shape, would come home for dinner. The husband actually didn't matter much to Tamara—what counted was the dinner and how she would serve it. She liked the glitter of her mother's sterling so she imagined the table set with candles and gleaming glasses and brilliant silver. Then she imagined herself dressed something like a queen in a long, white strapless

gown, with many floating layers of skirts, diamonds around her neck, and—the ecstasy of it
made her shiver with pleasure—a glittering tiara
set in her own short, red curls.

The daydream lasted for most of the walk
around the block until Celia spat out her dummy
and began to fuss. Then Tamara quickly wheeled
her home and was told by Martine to wash her
hands and help Rebecca set the table. Their father
would be coming home late—again—so there
wasn't any point in being fancy, Martine said.
They had scrambled eggs and toast and chocolate
milk. Neither Tamara nor her sisters got to see
much of their father; he was always away on
business, but Tamara loved him far more than
she loved her mother and carried around the
intensely pleasurable secret that she was his
favourite. He had told her that one day. He had
also told her that she would probably grow up to
be a famous movie star—she was that talented,
he had said in admiration, after watching her
embellish a school story with dramatic gestures
and an expressive voice. That was another one of
Tamara's fantasies—that she would sing and
dance her way to glory on the stage.

She thought her father was the handsomest
father in the whole of Fairfax. He was tall and
blond and strong. He had a deep, rich voice and
an infectious laugh. He knew how to do magic
tricks with cards and seemed to know precisely
what sort of wishes were close to the heart of a
little girl. He called her 'Tamara the Beautiful',
and she was convinced he was wonderful. She

knew Martine didn't think so, because her parents argued almost all the time they were together and, when they were apart she referred to Richard Clark as 'your father'.

That didn't bother Tamara because she didn't care much for Martine. Rebecca was the good sister, the obedient and thoughtful one, who helped with the dishes and didn't argue. Tamara, on the other hand, was irritating, disobedient and argumentative. She fought every restriction that Martine placed on her and every command. She wanted to wear what *she* wanted to wear, to comb her hair any way she pleased and to daydream at school if she were bored. She was often slapped for being a liar and put in her room for answering back. Tamara was too young to understand why she and Martine didn't get along; she only knew that she much preferred her father to her mother and her fantasy world to real life. The only time she graced the family with her undivided attention was when her father was home.

That night she played Monopoly with Rebecca, stole money from the bank when her sister wasn't looking and argued when it was time to go to bed. Then she got into her pyjamas, fooled around in her room until Martine got angry with her and finally succumbed to sleep. She was awakened much later when it was so dark out that she couldn't see anything in her room. Her father had come back from another sales trip, and the voices coming up from the living room were louder than usual so Tamara caught the occasional phrase or sentence.

'. . . selfish, unthinking . . .'

'I'm tired of being told what I should . . .'

'It's a lousy job and if you think I like spending day and night taking care of three . . .'

'You like the money . . . so extravagant that we . . .'

The voices always made her feel sick to her stomach, so Tamara put her hands over her ears and curled up into a tight ball under the covers. Then she slipped into a fantasy, a lovely, sweet-as-sugar fantasy that she was a world-famous ice skater, wearing one of those little skirts that stood straight out when you spun around. She carried a white fur muff that matched her ear-muffs and the cuffs of her costume. Her boots were white and the blades were a shiny silver. The reason she was a world-famous ice skater was because she twirled around faster than anyone else. She was so fast, she was a blur of rippling skirt, fur and flame-coloured hair. Oh, and her costume was also white with diamonds on a star shape in front—she had almost forgotten that. It was very important to get all the details right. Tamara spent a lot of time in her fantasies making sure that they were absolutely perfect.

The ice skater dream was so nice that it made her fall asleep despite the loudness of the voices still drifting up the stairs and through her door. Slowly, her hands dropped from her ears and she uncurled until she was lying flat on her back. The next time she was awakened the house was quiet and dark. But her door had opened and then shut again, letting in a faint strobe of light and a tall figure.

'Daddy?' she asked sleepily.

'Hi, doll,' he whispered. 'Mind if I come in with you for a few minutes?'

'No.'

They often cuddled together, on the couch or in the big chair beside the fireplace. Tamara liked the feel of her father's arms around her; she liked the scent of his shaving lotion and the rough feel of his beard against her cheek. So it didn't bother her when he slipped under the covers and gathered her up in his arms.

'How's my princess?' he asked.

'Good.'

'How was school today?'

'Not so good.'

'Why?'

'Mrs Contaigne made us do a spelling test and the words were so hard. I didn't know those words.'

'Hadn't you practised them before?'

'Uh-uh.'

'Maybe you weren't listening.'

'Daddy,' replied Tamara in an indignant whisper. 'I did, too.'

'Sure you did, honey. Sure you did.'

He hugged her closer and Tamara snuggled up against the crisp cotton of his pyjama top. Her father was stroking her hair and, closing her eyes, she began to fall asleep again, her body taking on that familiar feel of floating in the soothing, warm darkness of oblivion. She began to dream, or at first she thought she was dreaming. The hand on her hair disappeared, and another hand appeared; a warm hand that kept touching her, stroking her, caressing her. In that place. In that forbidden place of strange sensations. In that place that no one touched but Tamara herself. And the dream went on . . . and on . . . and on . . .

They were in Jake's bedroom by now. The lights had never been turned on and they were lying together in the dark, fully clothed, on top of the bedspread. Tamara sobbed quietly into Jake's shoulder while he held her tight, stunned by what she had said, trying to assimilate it, to understand what its repercussions had been. Of course, he had heard of incest, but he had never met anyone who had been a part of it. What had always seemed disgusting in the abstract, had taken on a new dimension for him. Tamara had told her story without the slightest theatrical decoration and the words, stark and skeletal, had made it that much more horrible.

'How long did it go on?' he asked shakily. It had shocked Jake to realise that had Tamara's father been standing before him, he would have killed him, without compunction, thought or remorse.

'On and off—for about two years.'

'You didn't tell anyone?'

'No. At first, I didn't understand it. I mean—he was my father and I loved him and trusted him. He told me it was all right and that it was our secret. Later, I got scared—of him, of what my mother would do if she found out, of what the world would think of me if it knew. And I was afraid that if I did say something or tried to stop him, he would turn to Rebecca or, even worse, Celia. Oh, she was just a baby, but what did I know? He seemed capable of anything.'

Jake felt the warmth of tears spreading on his shirt and he rocked her in his arms. 'Tam, I'm sorry. I'm so sorry.'

'My parents separated when I was eleven, and he took off after that. We never heard from him again. I've always known that what he did made me . . . made part of me hate men. You were right about that. But I wanted them, too. When I was seventeen, I started going out with this guy from a nearby community college. I was—well, technically a virgin, but I wanted desperately to be grown up so I started sleeping with him. Martine figured it out after I came home one night looking as if I'd been dragged through the bushes. She was furious with me, she called me horrible names, she accused me of sleeping with every boy I'd ever looked at twice. I'd always fought with Martine so I didn't think this was a new thing, it was just an argument with a new slant to it. Naturally I screamed back at her. And then she hit me with it.' Tamara paused and then took a deep breath. 'She told me that I had broken up her marriage, that my father had been infatuated with me, that she knew he had been crawling into my bed because she wouldn't let him in hers.'

'God.'

'She knew, Jake. She'd known all along and never done anything about it. You can't imagine how I hated her then. She called me a whore and a slut and a prostitute. She accused me, a child of nine, of seducing my own father. I ran away the next day. Rebecca cried, Celia stole a hundred dollars from Martine for me and I was gone. I couldn't stay in the same house with her anymore.'

She was shaking again, and Jake's arms tightened around her.

'I've always hated her,' Tamara said, 'but . . . sometimes I understand enough to feel sorry for her. She was—still is—very beautiful; she was an only child and very pampered. She must have expected more from my father than he could ever give her. But he didn't love her, he loved me, and she was jealous of that relationship.'

'But to accuse you of *seducing* your father.'

'She's not a rational woman; she never has been. And, it wasn't all her fault either. He was the one who committed the act. I think she made him feel so small and puny that he turned to me. It's easy to be powerful when you're an adult and your victim is a child.'

Jake sighed heavily. 'I can see why you've always shied away from any sort of family scene.'

Tamara placed her hand on his chest. 'I'm terrified of it,' she admitted in a small voice. 'It's the most frightening thing I can think of.'

Jake was silent for a second. 'Tell me something, Tam. Do you love me?'

'I . . . think so.'

'Nothing like a spot of confidence,' he said with a small, rueful laugh.

'I've never loved any man other than . . . him. All I know is that what I feel for you is different from what I've felt for the others. And you did make me jealous with Carla. If I hadn't been so pregnant, I wouldn't have been here when you came back. The idea of becoming Medea for a while was the only thing that saved my sanity.'

'I take back a bit of what I said, Tam. I thought you were a pretty powerful lady back there.'

Tamara sat up a bit, grabbed a tissue and blew her nose. 'But you were right. I never realised before that my acting was . . . just that—acting. How could I act the part of a lover or a mother or anything when I didn't have the first idea what emotions were involved? I was powerful as Medea tonight because, for the first time, I really knew how she must have felt. Jake, I've been an emotional cripple for so long.'

'You can act here, you know.' Jake cleared his throat, determined to keep any pleading out of his voice. 'Calgary isn't New York, but we do have a couple of small theatre companies. It wouldn't be a bad place to start.'

There was a heavy silence and then, 'You're suggesting I stay here?'

Jake reached up and switched on the light by the bed. He turned to Tamara then and smiled at her. She was an absolute mess. The mascara and eye-shadow had run down her cheeks and along her temples in multi-coloured streaks. Her hair was wild, standing on end, in every direction. A freckle here and there popped through her make-up, giving her a mottled look. She was a mess, but he loved her. And the knowledge that she loved him gave Jake a sudden belief that it would all work out the way he wanted. She might be terrified of families, and the concept of marriage might initially press all her panic buttons, but he once again had hope.

'Marry me,' he said.

Tamara blinked in the brightness. 'Why did you turn the light on?'

'Because I didn't feel like making my first proposal in the dark,' Jake said in a matter-of-fact voice. 'I wanted to make sure that I had the right woman.'

If he had thought to get a rise out of Tamara with that statement, Jake discovered that he was wrong. She ignored him and tried to smooth down her hair. 'I must look as if I've been run over by a bulldozer.'

'Worse,' he said agreeably.

'Oh, thanks.' She opened the drawer in the night-table on her side of the bed and pulled out a small mirror. 'God, you're right!' She got off the bed and waddled into the bathroom.

Jake propped himself up on one elbow and shouted over the sound of running water. 'Well? What do you think?'

The water stopped. 'I think I'm never going to wear eye-shadow again when I anticipate an evening of sentimental, tear-jerking slosh.'

Jake grinned to himself, hearing the old Tamara coming back. In the past hour, she had been terrified, panicky and revealed. He had seen the raw, painful wounds and had known a part of Tamara that she had never shown to anyone else. Now, just as if she were putting on a well-worn coat, she was covering up again, protecting herself from the outside world in the only way she knew how, by being iconoclastic, prickly and aggressive.

He could now hear the crackling of her hair as she brushed it. 'And what about getting married?'

Tamara appeared in the doorway. Her face had been scrubbed clean; her hair had been clipped back. She had gone from Medea to a small girl with a spray of freckles on each cheek, blue eyes tilted in pale orange lashes. If the idea of marriage frightened her, she hid it very well. Only her words gave Jake a hint of what she must be feeling. 'It doesn't necessarily follow,' she answered with a touch of disdain.

'What?'

'Being in love and getting married.'

'I don't think it's a bad arrangement. It has its good points; a hint of security, a pinch of companionship, a guaranteed bed partner.'

'I prefer living in sin.'

'I don't,' Jake replied firmly. 'I want to marry you.'

Tamara drew herself up. 'It's so predictable; it's so traditional.'

'I'm an old-fashioned sort of a guy. And I think your baby needs a predictable, traditional father.'

'You're trying to blackmail me,' she said in a warning tone.

Jake could see that Tamara wasn't going to come around easily. Not that he had expected that she would. She had too many memories that hurt, too many fears of commitment, too much distrust of the world around her. 'You don't have to say yes right now,' he offered. 'You've got plenty of time.'

'*Yes?*' At first, Jake thought that Tamara was going to let her fear and anger get the better of her, but then she gave him a flirtatious glance, put her hands on what remained of her hips, and said in an Irish brogue, 'And aren't you a wee bit presumptuous, Mr DeBlais, in thinkin' I might say yes.'

Jake leaned back against the pillows and crossed his arms beneath his head. He looked up at the ceiling and smiled at it in a knowing fashion. 'Nope,' he said. 'I'm not presumptuous at all.'

The delivery room was not a soft and warm place. It was painted a cold, hospital white and gleamed with chrome—on the overhead light, the forceps lying idle in a polished tray, the stirrups that held Tamara's knees wide apart. The pain had been bad, worse than she had expected, but she had already forgotten about it. The baby had been born seconds ago, slipping out into the doctor's hands, red and wet and already crying. A healthy boy, who would weigh in at eight pounds, five ounces. He also had a head of hair that, damp as it was, was obviously red. The nurse exclaimed over it as the doctor clipped the umbilical cord.

'Just like a carrot,' she declared over the baby's thin wails as she picked him up. 'Come on, sweetheart, let's see how big you are.'

Tamara strained to watch as the nurse carried him over to the scales on the side of the room. The two doctors were busy with the afterbirth and stitching her up, but she barely noticed. The baby had her whole attention; she couldn't keep her eyes off its round face, the plum-coloured fist waving in the air, the bowed scrawny legs.

'Kind of homely, isn't he?' she whispered to Jake who had been standing at her head during the delivery, his hand gripping hers.

Jake wiped the sweat from his forehead. 'He's gorgeous and you know it. God, Tam, what are women made of? I don't think I could have gone through that myself.'

'It always amazes the fathers,' the nurse commented. 'Makes them respect their wives more.' She had weighed the baby, cleaned him and efficiently wrapped him in a white receiving blanket. Now, she offered the baby to Jake. 'Want to hold him?'

Tamara could hear Jake swallowing. 'Me?'

'He won't bite,' the nurse answered with a smile. 'Come on, Dad, you can do it.' The baby stopped crying as he was put into Jake's arms. He blinked a few times and then stared up at Jake with eyes of the deepest blue. The fact that they were slightly crossed didn't take away from the ferocity of his infantile concentration. 'See,' the nurse went on, 'it's easier than you think.'

Jake's laugh was a bit shaky. 'Yeah, I guess so.'

The sight of her son in Jake's arms did something to Tamara's heart. She had not known if she truly loved him; she had fought any suggestion of his that they get married. It had seemed to her during the week between her confession to Jake and the birth of her baby that every doubt she had ever had about marriage and families had come to the surface, bringing with it more fear and greater apprehension. Jake hadn't mentioned marriage to her again so her struggle had been a silent one. She had been pulled this way and that, indecision had held her in its terrible grip. She didn't want to say yes, but somehow she couldn't say no either.

In the past, when she had thought of leaving Calgary, she had been very careful not to think that she would also be leaving Jake. She had looked at it from a different perspective; in fact, she hadn't used the word 'leaving' to herself. She had thought of it as returning to New York, as going back home. But now the realisation that a couple of thousand miles would lie between them and that Jake would no longer be a part of her daily life hurt far more than she had ever imagined. She had begun to wonder if all the excitement and glamour of Manhattan would make up for the fact that she was once more, baby or not, essentially alone.

But she wasn't sure if her dream of being a famous actress would ever die. She understood now that it was a fantasy—like all of her others —fed by her own imagination and her father's praise, but she had tempered it into an adult fantasy and it had given her the drive and ambition to attempt what few small-town girls had ever tried. Manhattan would always lure her; she knew that and, while there were theatres in Calgary, none of them matched the grandeur of the Broadway stage. Tamara was wise enough about herself to know that no matter how happy she might be if she were married to Jake, there would always be a part of her that would mourn what she no longer had.

And the thought of committing herself to a domestic life terrified her. She couldn't help it. Her experience of her parents' marriage had been a bad one; her father had traumatised her for life. There would always be an aspect of Tamara that would cower in the darkness of her soul. It was the place of demons and fears and horror. She usually had it clamped down and well hidden, but at times the demons would break loose and come to haunt her. That dizzying sensation that she was alone in a world of enemies would come back; the profound belief in her own guilt would wash over her again. Intellectually, Tamara had always blamed her father for what had happened; emotionally, she had often blamed herself. What father seduces his own daughter except one who has been enticed and flirted with? It had never been enough for her to understand that she had, like any other daughter, loved her father in a sexual as well as a paternal way or that, like other little girls, she had tried out her fledgling feelings of femininity on what should have been the safest man in her world. The fact that he was unbalanced enough to return that love in the most brutal way a father could had never quite obliterated Tamara's guilt. It had left a scar within her that would never heal.

Yet, she knew with the certainty of a woman who has suffered at many male hands that Jake was the only man in the world with whom she could hope to have a normal, married existence. He offered to her all the love and affection she had never had; his personality as neatly interlocked with hers as if they were pieces in a jigsaw puzzle. It no longer seemed to matter that their tastes were so different. Tamara had learned to rely on his calm nature, his amiability, his humour and his patience. She had come to enjoy the way she could astonish him and then make him smile. His laughter was precious to her. And, for the first time in her life, she had a sexual existence that was warm, passionate and satisfying. That had never happened to her before, and she treasured it, knowing it for what it was —a rare jewel.

She had teetered on the edge of decision as the last week of her pregnancy dragged itself out. She had tried to weigh every fact and fear in a logical balance; she had mentally made a list of pros and cons, but she had discovered that the choice of marrying Jake or returning to New York was never going to be made on any rational ground. So Tamara hesitated—it was as if she were waiting for a sign to tell her the direction her life would take. She didn't know if one would come, but it did, along with the pains that started late one night, sharp, hurtful contractions that made Tamara sigh with relief that the baby was finally on its way. She woke Jake up, they timed the contractions, called the doctor when they were five minutes apart and left for the hospital at the three-minute mark. By the time she was in the labour room, she was already dilated six centimeters; the birth finally took place early in the afternoon.

The nurse had now gone around to stand by the doctors who were doing the final stitches of the episiotomy. Tamara and Jake were left looking at one another with the bundle of baby lying quiescent between them.

'Marry me?' he asked.

Tamara was hardly aware of the sudden attention they were receiving from the other end of the bed. 'I'm still thinking,' she replied hesitantly.

'I don't want to give him up,' Jake said.

Tamara couldn't resist the Irish brogue again. 'So—it was the babe you wanted all along.'

His hand gripped hers. 'And you, too.' She was silent. 'Please, Tam. Say yes.'

One of the doctors smiled. 'For heaven's sake, Tamara, make up your mind. We can't concentrate down here.'

A great bubble of laughter rose within her. It held the euphoria that comes after childbirth, a sudden certainty that what she would say would be right and proper, and a vast amusement that she, of all people, would be making the most momentous decision of her life on an unexpectedly absurd stage—the hospital bed where she had delivered her son. She had an audience, too; three interested observers who had stopped what they were doing to watch the show. Of course, she couldn't resist it. If nothing else, Tamara was an actress. The Irish brogue continued. 'I don't come to you pure,' she confessed, giving the 'r' in pure a full-scale roll.

'Tam.'

'And I bring the burden of child.' Everyone was smiling now. Even Jake—who looked like he wanted to throttle her. 'But I suppose if you'll have me, knowing as how I'm no bargain—well then, the answer is yes.'

'Amen,' said the nurse and the three heads bent down again.

Jake glared at her. 'I'm considering taking back my offer.'

'You wouldn't,' she said softly.

The baby stirred in his arms and blinked those trusting, blue eyes at him again. 'No,' he whispered, 'I wouldn't.'